ON THE
WIND

WHISPERS ON THE WIND

MARSHA G. COOK

IE Snaps
by
IngramElliott

Whispers on the Wind
Copyright © 2020 Marsha G. Cook

Published by IngramElliott, Inc.
www.ingramelliott.com
9815-J Sam Furr Road, Suite 271, Huntersville NC 28078

This is a work of fiction. The names, characters, places, or events used in this book are the product of the author's imagination or used fictitiously. Any resemblance to actual people (alive or deceased) events, or locales is completely coincidental.

Book design by Maureen Cutajar, gopublished.com
Cover design by: H.O. Charles

ISBN Paperback: 978-1-7328436-8-4
ISBN E-Book: 978-1-7328436-9-1

Library of Congress Control Number: 2020931577

Subjects: Fiction—General. Fiction—Metaphysical and Visionary. Fiction—Young Adult.

Published in the United States of America.
Printed in the United States of America.
First Edition: 2020, First International Edition: 2020

Dedication

I wish to express an abiding and profound thankfulness to my greatest support, soft place to fall and all around love, Gary; and to Heidi, without whom the birth and life of a place such as The Nook would not exist, my deepest gratitude. You are both always in my heart!

Prologue

The mist is heavy all around me. There's a sense of emptiness, and it feels as though I'm alone. Yet in the haze are the shapes of many people. I want to see them clearly. I blink my eyes, try to clear the fogginess blurring everything, but I still can't see beyond the haze. Maybe I'm not being pure enough in my intention. Maybe I'm blocking them because right now I'm scared to death. I'm terrified because I can feel that there's a darkness hovering. It's like a rain-soaked storm cloud—dense, thick, and ominous. The energies are menacing and threatening. I don't like this; I don't like this at all. Maybe it's all my imagination. If it is, then I could just change my thoughts. No, no, not my imagination; I know I'm asleep. I'm dreaming. I'm dreaming a nightmare, and I can't seem to turn it off.

The veils begin to part, and I see now that I'm not alone. I'm not me either; at least not me as I am today. I'm a much younger version of myself, almost four years old. To celebrate my upcoming birthday, my family and I are at the beach in Atlantic City. The sun is shining, the waters of the Atlantic Ocean are shimmering, and the waves at the moment are gently rolling in and out. They sneak up to the beach and just as quickly, slide away. The sun has heated the ocean and turned it into a warm, caressing touch. As the waves slide in, they tickle me.

My daddy is helping me build a sandcastle right near the water's edge. I have four big pink buckets, two bright yellow shovels, and every seashell I can find nearby to build up my castle. My swimsuit is deep purple with white polka dots and has puffy, frilly little shoulder caps. Mommy makes me wear a big floppy hat to keep the sun from burning my head, face, and shoulders. My impatience is showing because the floppy brim is getting in my way. Every time I look down to pour water on the sand, it falls over my eyes. Daddy laughs at my pouts and grunts. He has a big, deep, rolling laugh that delights me and makes me feel loved and safe and happy, and I laugh just because he does. Actually, there's lots of laughter at the beach, lots of noise too because there are people everywhere. Some are on blankets; some are under big beach umbrellas; some are just in the sun.

As my castle grows ever taller, the sky seems to grow darker. The clouds are taking over, blocking the sunshine. Voices drift over the crowds.

"We are the darkness; we are here to harvest. We will take those we wish to have."

There are hands coming out of the clouds. Big, ugly, wrinkled, fat hands, and they're plucking people off the beach.

"Not my daddy and mommy!" I scream. "Not my daddy and mommy!"

But the hands move closer and closer to them. They're lifted away from the beach, away from me.

Then I hear a voice I don't know, and the air smells like sweet tobacco. "Hold on, Meems," the voice whispers. "You will be okay."

My parents have vanished along with many others, even the beach fades away. The darkness disappears too, and now I really am alone. I open my mouth to call out to my mom and dad. Instead I just scream and scream and scream.

1

Love Never Dies

Today is *the* day. The longer I lounge in my bed, the longer I can put this day off. The sun is shining in on me through the window where the breeze slips silently in and buffs my face like a soft caress. Oh, how I like that. It's time to stretch, to get moving, to grab hold of the day. I'd rather dawdle. I'm good at dawdling.

Wiggling, I can feel the silk of my comforter slither along my bare legs. My gran picked out this comforter. We went shopping at a fancy linen store to get just the right things a girl needs for her room, "her sanctuary," she had said. We picked a gentle lavender color with blues and mint greens. They matched the fluorite tower I had received on my thirteenth birthday. Next to amethyst, it's my favorite gemstone. Gran said the colors of my room would lend to healing when I needed it. She's always saying things like that, like, "Everyone needs their own sacred space to go to."

Here are some of the stories Gran has told over the years. I can hear her voice coming to a whisper as she reminds me that I know it's time to awaken my many "clairs." I was told as a little one that I "knew" things. I'd announce to the whole house that someone was about to ring the doorbell. In stores, I'd walk up to perfect strangers, lay my little hand on theirs, and tell them to stop worrying, or that everything would be okay, and sometimes I'd be spirited enough tell them to go to the doctor. Apparently, the family never knew what would happen when we were out in public.

Bringing a cup of hot peppermint tea to my room as I dawdle, Gran tucks her legs under her in my big, cushy chair, and I can practically read her mind as she reminisces. The picture in her head is as clear as a bell. A few months before my fourth birthday I had a terrible nightmare where I awakened screaming, "Not my daddy and mommy," over and over again. Shortly after my fourth birthday my parents, her daughter and son-in-law, were killed by a drunk driver. That was when I stopped "seeing and feeling" the things that made me "precognizant and psychic." I know; I know; it's time for me to reawaken these "things." Where better than a visit to the Seekers of Spirit, Mind, and Body Expo! Give me a break!

Gran exits my room with her empty mug of tea and a tilt of her head, so I move to the bathroom, still lost in thought. Gran is all I have. Mom and Dad made their transition when I was four. "Made their transition" is another of those things Gran says about death. Once, when I was angry about both my mom and dad leaving me, I yelled that they had been ripped from my life, that they had died, not transitioned. She raised an eyebrow and asked what I thought I knew about death. That stopped my outburst as fast as running into a wall stops your forward momentum. Though I had no idea what she meant when she said it, it did, I recall quite clearly, effectively shut me up and shut me down.

I will say I have marveled at and enjoyed my room these last four years; it has been my haven, my soft place to fall, my space to escape. I'm a kid, mostly, you know, and I really need my own soft space!

I love music. My iPod is my favorite toy! I listen to hip-hop, rap, opera, Broadway show tunes, and meditation music. I even have some oldies, like really old from the 1950s and '60s. Okay, I have what they used to call dance music loaded too. I'm crazy about all kinds of art, can't stand gardening, and cooking is just okay. I love to bake. My brownies are to die for!

My biggest secret...I can hear and see things. You know, like woo-woo kinds of things. Sometimes I hear voices all around me, kind of like little whispers. The voices are never clear, so I don't pay much attention to them. Then there are the times I see shadows move. Not my own shadow, shadows like wisps floating around just out of the corner of my eye. When I mention these kinds of things to Gran, she always nods sagely at me and says, "And?" I don't know where she wants me to go with that question, so I usually shrug and walk away. Then I avoid making direct eye contact for a few days and the woo-woo stuff goes away.

I have three best friends; Gran is my very best friend. She gets me. I don't have to explain myself to her, ever. She's cheered for me at every softball and soccer game I've played. She's patched my skinned knees, argued with my fussiest teachers, baked a million or more chocolate chip cookies for my school fairs, and shares my love for the old television show *Little House on the Prairie*. She says I'm her heart, and I know she's mine!

About three months ago, Gran started coughing. She couldn't catch her breath. After turning her into the proverbial pincushion, the doctors said she had cancer. We learned that there are two major types of lung cancer—non-small cell lung cancer and small cell lung cancer. They have far more complicated names that I don't care to memorize. Symptoms include coughing, chest pain, wheezing, and weight loss. These symptoms often don't appear until the cancer is advanced. That's exactly what happened to Gran. She thought she had chest congestion from allergies and it would go away. I kept asking her why she was losing weight and she told me she was getting her girlish shape back.

The treatments they wanted to use started with surgery. She really didn't want to "go under the knife"; I think she had a feeling it would hurry her cancer along. Then they suggested she also do chemotherapy (targeted drug therapy is the new lingo) or radiation therapy, and immunotherapy. Immunotherapy supports the chemo (we had to look it up to even know what the medical people were talking about); it's the "treatment of a disease by inducing, enhancing, or suppressing an immune response." In other words, it stops the body from responding to the drugs by attacking itself. So, you need drugs to kill the cancer and then drugs to soothe the first drugs so they don't kill you. I shouldn't have to know all this stuff! I don't want it in my head. It's too heavy to carry in my heart.

We began to have long talks about her leaving. Not just the day-to-day mess of paying bills and keeping up with the house and getting myself to school, the spiritual aspects of her "transition." I hate that word! We're talking death here. Deep, down both of us knew her diagnosis didn't give her a year to stay.

I'm a senior in high school and getting ready to graduate in the spring. Our plans were for me to go away to school after the summer. I have a job after school filing at a local law office. They were nice and offered me a full-time summer job to put money away for school. After graduation I was going to leave home for the first time and venture off to a place they call Happy Valley. The location is actually State College, PA. That's where the Pennsylvania State University is located. We call it Penn State. All my "Philly" girlfriends want to go to Penn State's main campus, University Park. In the old days that was where the football jocks would go to school, and a girl could find a husband fast! I want to go to Penn State because I love the mountains and the beautiful old buildings on the main campus. Plus, I did so well on my SATs and have such a high grade-point average (4.5) I managed to secure a four-year fully paid scholarship. Everything including housing is covered. Gran and I had a party when we received that news. We had lavender, mint green, and blue cupcakes with mint chocolate-chip ice cream.

I'm not sure Gran will make it to June when I graduate. I think my heart is breaking. And if she does live, how can I leave? She needs me as I have needed her these many years. How will I live without her? She says she will always be with me. I want her here, on the earth, right beside me as she's always been. It's not fair.

2

So Much More

Well, these rambling thoughts have given me an extra fifteen minutes to put off the inevitable. I should probably be thinking positive thoughts about today. Honestly, it scares me. Gran has always been able to "know" things other people can't, don't, and won't. Things like what kind of year I'm going to have once my birthday arrives, and she knows a tremendous amount of information about stones and healing.

I watch Gran working at the altar she set up in her bedroom as she works her magic with candles, gemstones, family pictures, and heirloom trinkets. Then there's the times when she has answers she couldn't possibly have looked up anywhere. Today we take the first step to awaken my "gifts." I know I need to understand that there is so much more than "we the people" can see with our three-dimensional eyes and know with our brains. Gran believes with all her heart that we are all much more than we realize. I need to remember, as she is always reminding me, that I am so much more.

Feeling better between chemo treatments, and a little stronger, Gran's turned her sights on me. We're off to Fairmount Park where the first official World's Fair in the United States was held. They called it the Centennial International Exhibition of 1876. Some of the original buildings are still in use today, and one of these beautiful old buildings, actually the main hall, will play host to the Seekers of Spirit, Mind, and Body this weekend. Honestly, I feel as though I'm being dragged kicking and screaming. It's so unfair and so weird.

She says I need to start my journey toward my inner light so when she leaves, we can still communicate. I know she's been doing that woo-woo stuff all her life, and I don't have a problem with that, but why does she want me to do it too? I'll lose all my friends; I just know it. Well, maybe not all. Some of us played with Gran's Ouija board (her spirit talking board) a while back. We had the house to ourselves, so we lit a bunch of candles, brought out the board, and turned off the lights. It kind of freaked us out when the heart-shaped planchette started moving of its own accord. The planchette is the answer indicator. I asked about Gran's health. With my fingertips barely touching it, the darned thing moved right to the bottom of the board where it said "Goodbye." Like I said, I was freaked!

Now I'm going to meet people who say they do this spirit communication thing all the time. They call themselves psychic, intuitive mediums. I mean really? What could I possibly learn from that weird woo-woo bunch?

Bucks County, where we live, in an area that still has farmland, is about an hour's ride to Philly. Driving into the city is never fun. I pretty much give the keys to our Honda CRV to Gran and say, "Go for it." The road we take last is called the Schuylkill Expressway, it's also known as the "Sure kill Expressway." Use your imagination on that nickname.

3

Seekers

Well, here we are at Fairmount Park. I'm blown away by all the cars already here. I guess there are a lot of people interested in this seekers event or the psychic stuff. Even the building looks like its shimmering, kind of waving. With big arches, Memorial Hall, as the locals call it, has a crystal dome at its rooftop center. Maybe that's why the entry looks so alive with movement. Maybe the crystal takes energy from the sun and spreads it around. The main blocks of the building are granite. Then there's iron and glass everywhere. Being that the place is well over one hundred years old, I'm thinking the original builders knew what they were doing. Gran says the crystal dome is reflecting the energy of all the people.

Once we finally clear the ticket booth, Gran grabs my hand, squeezes, and says, "Here we are, Meems." She calls me Meems. So do my friends. My name is Mary Elizabeth Emily Mearcham. So, my initials are M-E-E-M.

I stop and look around. It's so crowded and noisy, I can barely breathe. There are lots of rows of booths, as far as the eye can see—rows! Some have magnificent gemstone displays. I could stay at those booths all day. The stones and I get along in a way I can't explain to anyone else.

They soothe me—energize me—make me feel lit up from the inside. Gran said we were going to "look over" all the readers to see which one we will sit with for a reading. When she says "we" she means "me." I'm supposed to get a "vibe"—a pull, a warm, fuzzy feeling—and that will be my signal to talk to that specific person. Honestly, some of these people scare me! There's an ancient lady (really, really old) who's all bent over. I think she's so bent because she has so much hair on her head. It's all wrapped in rags, frizzy and huge. I'm afraid she might be hiding a crow or something in her hair and it will get me if I get too close. I saw the old Alfred Hitchcock movie *The Birds*, so I know what they can do to a person!

There's a lady who has so much black eye makeup on, she looks like a ghoul. She's dressed like the gypsies you used to see in old movies—peasant blouse, lots of gold chains and bangles, and giant hoop earrings. She's weird, too. Who would trust anyone looking like that?

Gran says, "You never judge a book by its cover, Meems."

I say, "Ugh."

On we go. Up and down every aisle. I'm not feeling drawn to anyone yet, though we have some ways to go. I'm secretly keeping an eye on Gran, so she doesn't overdo it. She'd be upset with me if she believed that I thought she was performing at anything less than her usual stellar capacity! I can't help but worry. Though worrying feels like a big hand of darkness hovering over me.

There's something I haven't shared with anyone yet; one of my favorite things is the moon. When she's full, I can stare at her for hours. I miss her when she's dark. Then, when she comes into a left-side crescent, I know it's time to let go of old habits and things that no longer serve to honor the inner me. And, when she's a crescent to the right, I make plans because I know she will bring me to a prosperous place. And all that stuff works!

I'm thinking about the moon because I'm in front of a booth that has a beautiful blue banner with a full moon right in the center. Gran said to look for signs or symbols that "moved" me. She said I would "know"; I would be drawn toward something or someone when I had found the reader meant for me. I think this is it. The name under the moon is The Nook. In my mind I'm thinking that means small, private, comfy. Gran is speaking with the essential oil people directly on the other side of the aisle. That gives me a chance to watch the ladies in the moon booth, see what they're doing and how they're interacting with the people sitting with them. I would feel creepy if they felt me staring.

The ladies in the booth are around my gran's age. I think that's good. It feels like they've been around the business awhile and know what they're doing, and they aren't weird to look at. The people who are sitting with them greet them like old friends and they're all laughing, crying, and hugging, though they do seem serious as they take people's hands and lay cards on the table. I like how they look directly into the eyes of the person they're reading for. They look like they're making a sincere connection, almost as if the whole pavilion fades away and it's only them and the people that have sat down with them.

Gran has purchased a collection of oils and she's ready to move on. I'm not going to tell her about this booth yet. She's waiting for me to give her a signal. I want to walk through all the aisles first and then decide. This is, after all, my first psychic, woo-woo reading. I'm going to be extremely choosey, Gran shows me her purchases and says she's glad we stopped at that booth, says the essential oils people really know their oils.

4

Artie and Bitsy

The morning has slipped by in a blur. We walked all over the place and Gran needs to sit, so we're going outside to the magnificent gardens. I'm glad this is a spring show. The gardens are filled with sections of rhododendron, azaleas, tulips, pansies, and some of my very favorites, honeysuckle and gardenias. The scent of the air is to die for! We brown-bagged lunch (so Gran can eat clean) and have found a lovely bench in the middle of all this color and sunshine, so this is where we'll park it for our lunch break.

All too soon, eating time is over and Gran is asking if I saw anything that caught my eye. It's time to tell her about the moon banner booth and the two ladies there. Why do I feel like this is a confession? What do I have to feel guilty about? Here goes!

"So, did you notice the booth across from the essential oils people?" I ask.

She nods and I continue.

"I kind of felt something at that booth. Most of the booths didn't give me a feeling one way or the other, except those whose energies felt spooky. But this one really got my attention with their moon banner and the way the two ladies were interacting with the people sitting with them. They weren't wearing headsets and didn't have fancy gear on their tables; it was really…just them. I think I liked that and would maybe go meet them. Want to walk over to that part of the building with me? I don't want to go alone, but you might be too tired; in which case I'm good to go home."

Gran grinned at that last part, stood up, reached out toward me with her right hand, waiting for me to slide my left hand into hers, and when I did, gave me a tug toward the building.

The booth is up ahead, and both ladies are taking a break and standing in the aisle. Geesh, it's time to take the plunge. As we approach, the taller lady steps forward to ask if we'd like to sample the art of palmistry. That's cool. Next thing I know she's taken my bags out of my hands and tucked my arm under hers.

Pulling me in close and pressing on my thumbs, she says, "My name is Artie, and oh my, aren't we a bit on the stubborn side?"

Gran's laughing. "Yes, she is, always has been."

Artie asks if I am right- or left-handed and goes on to explain that since I'm a "righty" my left hand is my hand of destiny, my plans for when I came to earth, and my right hand is my hand of action. She says, "That's where the choices you are making are recorded. The lines on your right palm can change every six months."

She goes on to tell me that I came to be a healer, I am deeply intuitive, and my life is going to be a very long one. After one last squeeze in the center of each hand, she also tells me I'm healthy and strong and I will be okay. I can tell you she's got my attention. Gran doesn't want her palm read; I think she's afraid Artie will know how sick she is and say something Gran thinks I don't already know.

The other lady is standing there with little cards in her hand. I ask what they are. She tells me they are word wizardry cards and if I choose one, she will give me a free mini reading. What have I got to lose? I close my eyes, sweep my hand over the cards like I know what I'm doing, and choose one. It's green camouflage and the word in the center of the card is *trust*. The lady asks me my name, takes my hand, looks directly into my eyes, and pulls me away from Gran as she says, "Grandma, we're going over here a bit to have a very private discussion."

Gran nods and begins a conversation with Artie.

"Sweetie, my name is Elishabet. Everyone calls me Bitsy.

Let's talk about the card you chose."

She explains to me that she "sees" that my heart is wrapped up tight in a net, covered by camouflage so no hurt can get in. Bitsy tells me that because I have put a lock on my heart, I've let go of my trust in myself and the world. Then she tells me that trust is all about what's inside me, not about the outside world or the people in it. She says I need to trust that when life knocks me to my knees, I'll get up and keep moving forward; I need to unlock my heart and give my love to the one who needs it the most right now, and that the one who needs it most is me. And when I can give it to me, I'll be able to share it with others, especially Gran.

How could she possibly know all that? How could Artie know I needed to hear I'd be alright? It dawns on me, as tears spring to life in my eyes, that there's something to this psychic-medium thing; there's more than we can see with our three-dimensional eyes and know with the brain in our head. As the tears well up, Bitsy asks if she can hug me. I nod, and she takes me in her arms like we've know each other forever. It feels good. This is where I'll have my first reading, in the booth with the full moon and the two ladies who feel like—well, like grandmothers. Actually, now I want a reading with Bitsy and Artie both! I wonder, will Gran splurge on two readings?

22

5

Reading the Woo-Woo

As if I've actually spoken those words out loud, Gran's eyes are drawn to mine and she sees the dawning of new thoughts creating sparkles in the blue depths of my eyes. Artie has a reading already sitting at her table, so I sit down with Bitsy. She begins by telling me that her guides know it's time to go to work when she asks me to sign her contact book.

As I lift the pen, she begins the gentlest prayer I've ever heard. "Father, Mother, God, we thank you for these moments together and ask for only the highest and best." Then she whispers something about creating a circle of protection. She tells me that she will mail me a postcard when the Seekers Expo comes back to Philly. If I come see her with the card, I'll get a discount on my next reading with her.

We start with my birthday and I begin to learn about numerology. Bitsy explains, "Before you were born, your brilliant soul sent you a letter. You wrote it into the stars and into the fabric of every energy, everything. Numerology is the study of reading those letters to the self. When the month and day of your birthday is added together with the current year, we will know what kind of year you will have."

My birthday is December third. That's a twelve and a three. So, we start with a fifteen, which is added together to arrive at a six. Then a two is added (2018 = 2, 2 + 0 + 1 + 8 = 11 / 2). This all adds up to an eight, which will begin in December on my birthday. Bitsy says that means I'm currently in a seven year—a year of questions. Am I doing the right things, at the right time, in the right place? Am I with the right people, am I making good decisions, will I lose everything that matters to me most? Wow, that hits the nail on the head! She says that's the "mundane" explanation of a seven and goes on to explain there is an esoteric meaning as well. The number seven year represents a deep inner life, introspection, sacred silence and solitude and the flowering of one's spirituality. A seven year challenges a person to heed their inner guidance. Oh geesh, that sure explains what I had come to think of as my craziest thoughts. We've just begun and I'm blown away already. She also says that when I get to my birthday at the end of the year I will then enter an eight year, one of power and prosperity; the budding individual here attunes to the law of spirit and brings to their life an understanding of personal authority and the limitless, boundless, continuity of the infinite soul.

Me? That's all I can think. *Me?*

And then Bitsy says, "It doesn't matter how old you are."

Whoa, she's in my head, reading my thoughts.

She asks if I have any questions, and at this point I'm so dumbfounded, I simply move my head from side to side. I'm speechless! A washable pink pen comes out and Bitsy reaches for my hands. "Time for palmistry," she says.

I tell her I already know about my left hand being my hand of destiny and my right being my hand of action. Without batting an eye, she takes my hands in hers and starts pressing on my thumbs. One bounces and moves quite easily, but the other won't budge. Bitsy chuckles and tells me there are times when I am extremely stubborn like an oak tree, and other times when I'm as flexible in my thinking as a willow tree. Funny, Gran's said the same thing for years. Sometimes I'll look at every angle of a problem to find the best way over, under, or around it. Then, at other times, I get a thought about something and nothing, nothing, nothing can change my mind!

She goes on to show me the mark of the healer (four parallel lines right under my pinkie), that I'm highly intuitive (lots of little *T*s on the meaty part of my palm), and then she fills in three lines that make a triangle in the middle of my palm. She tells me this is the mystic triangle. It means I'm on a deeply spiritual path; I've come knowing I'll make choices based on what will be the highest and best for all the people in my life. My triangles (one in each hand) are big and indicate that my spiritual path will be intense.

Bitsy points out that I love to travel, and that I have lines indicating I am a magnetic, charismatic person. She tells me how many "loves of the heart" I planned, how many children I decided I might have, and how I ruminate over every conversation I have. That means I repeat it over and over in my head. Yeah, that would be me. I can remember everything anyone has ever said to me, and how they said it; one could say I'm a deep thinker, or as my friends say, a cud chewer!

6

Word Wizardry Nitty-Gritty

Next, Bitsy takes out a big handful of her little cards and shuffles them. As she shuffles, she explains that each card has a different color that corresponds to the seven chakras of the body; some have designs, some have solid backgrounds, and each word has a font that may be thin or thick, script or block. Continuing, she tells me that the colors, words, designs, and fonts paint a picture in her mind's eye, and from this picture her clairvoyance, clairaudience, and clairsentience bring information from the astral plane and show her details not of this dimension. The information tells her a story, which she translates for me. I'm so ready to see this in action again!

She makes three vertical lines and counts out seven cards in each line. One, she says, represents information describing the past, the middle is the present, and the last is the future. One by one, she turns over each card so we can see the colors, designs, and words. Though not nearly as fancy as some of the beautiful decks of tarot cards I've seen, they seem to have a depth and glow. We both notice there are a lot of purple cards. That means third eye and crown chakra colors: intuition, connection to source, higher self. She closes her eyes, takes a deep breath, and begins to explain the meaning of the cards of the past.

I take a picture of the cards with my phone so I can go over them again later. Here are the seven words: *compassionate*, purple with a solid background; *dependable*, purple with little flowers; *winter*, green with polka dots, though I notice some of the dots are missing; *gentle*, purple with a light and dark striped background; *plucky*, green with the light and dark stripes; and *wisdom*, blue with little flowers.

Bitsy explains that the purple compassion card describes the time of my parents' passing and my need for the understanding and patience that my gran gave so freely. The purple with flowers on the word *dependable* indicates that though I felt alone, I wasn't. Gran said that all the time. "You have me," she'd say whenever I had a meltdown.

Bitsy continued; the green card with the word *winter* and the missing dots referred to me feeling life had entered a dark phase that felt like it had ended, and I had no idea what would happen to me, when or how. She said, "You expected to be 'out in the cold' and alone during this period."

We continued with the stripes on the purple card reading *gentle*, which means that you had days where you felt okay and others when you questioned your existence. There are two of these cards because for so long, your days were unbalanced and your need was great. She said, "Plucky means when life knocks you down, you get up again and again because you have an amazing inner strength."

So, okay, now it's like she lived with me and Gran and listened to our conversations, or at least she heard the things Gran said to me!

"The last card," she says. "Wisdom, in blue with flowers, means baby step by baby step you talked through, cried out, and came to a place that held energies of inner peace. You came to accept that life had come to an ending of sorts, it had totally changed, and you had to change to move forward. And you knew deep inside that you would create a new life as a result of all the change."

Wow, I hadn't even told my best friends all that was going on in my life, running through my head, filling my thoughts.

Bitsy moved on to the center row of words. On the top of the row was a solid purple card with the word *spiritual* in big, fat letters. Next was a solid, bright green card with the word *loving*, then another solid purple card with the word *winter*, followed by the word *summer* in bright orange camouflage with really wide letters. Then another *summer* card, this one in solid purple, and last another purple card with little flowers surrounding the word *compassionate*. Knowing that these words would reflect where I am today, I couldn't wait for Bitsy to begin.

She asked if I knew what an old soul I am and how strong my inner voice is. That, of course, was the meaning of the first card. She said if I was struggling to find an answer, all I needed to do was quiet my brain chatter and seek the answer in my heart. She asked me to listen to the wisdom in my core, the encyclopedia of knowledge I had created through my many lifetimes.

The gentle card, she continued, represents the way I see moving through the world around me. The card is a deep purple and she said it means I am truly connected to the divine within. Okay, so at this point in time, I am fried, wondering if I am all she says I am! Truthfully, I spend a lot of my time scared. I don't have a lot of close friends. The kids I go to school with all have parents, and even the ones whose parents are divorced, at least they have them. I didn't get to do the father-daughter dances, or have my mom work like a crazed cupcake queen for the school bake sales.

Because Gran has always had to work, I was the one who didn't have a family member to chaperone me and my schoolmates on school trips. Rather than feel the loneliness, I simply retreated into myself and basically put up walls. I mean, I'm not pathetic or anything like that. Me and my gal pals hang at the mall, go to the movies, and polish our nails together, and when we were kids, we played together all the time. It's just that I feel so different. Now Bitsy is telling me I'm super special.

The next card is the word *winter* in red camouflage. Bitsy tells me how I've shielded myself from the group I hang out with. She says they don't know how much of myself I hide. It's like she's reading my thoughts. This is too spooky. She also says I'd hibernate like a bear in winter if I could. Since the color red represents the root chakra, and that's all about the "tribe" as she calls it, when winter brings the cold weather, she says, I'm ready to stay home— alone. Well, yeah, I am!

The next card is in orange camo with the word *summer*, which, she informs me, means it's time to cast off my cloak of invisibility and work on letting more of the world in. This summer is the time for me to spread my wings and see what the big, wide world has to offer. Huh! Then she says the final card—*compassionate* in purple with flowers—means that as I do spread my wings, I need to pay attention to all of my feelings and when needed, stay close to home. I also need to make plans for some summer adventures and be good to myself. I look her in the eye and in my bossiest tone of voice I let her know I have no idea how to plan adventures, let alone treat myself as anything special and good. It's not that I don't like myself, I do. But love myself, really? What could she possibly mean by that? I *love* Gran, I love my room, and I *love* my books. How could feelings like that be applied to me? Guess I do have a lot to learn. I sure hope Gran hangs around to help.

7

And the Future Will Be

We are now up to the third row of word cards. The first word is *spring*—it's camo purple. Next is *compassionate*—the writing is calligraphy script and the background is blue wavy lines. Third is a purple card with big, fat, white letters and the word is *happy*. Another card with a solid, deep purple background next, with the word *dependable*. Green flowers with *magical* in script is the next card. The sixth card is purple too, with big white letters and the word *healing*. Last is another *compassionate* card, green with polka dots, some of the dots are missing. So, these cards represent what hasn't come yet, the future. Bitsy looks at me and asks if I'm ready.

"Sure," I answer with my best bravado. Inside, I hear, *Yeah sure*. If I were adding an emoticon, it would be a frowning face.

She says, "When spring comes you will want to hide away, continue your winter hibernation. It will be a very spiritual time for you, and you will need to bring your empathy from the inner to the outer world. The best way to do that will be to speak your truth. You will waver, question yourself as to whether or not you should speak up. The answer is yes, you will need to use your voice. When you run into the words *should*, *would*, and *could*, go around them. Choose the path that represents the highest and best for you. If *should*, *would*, and *could* pop up, they are weak platforms to avoid. When you think you *should* be doing something, saying something, being something, the *should* indicates your fear and holds you back. When you use the word *would* there is something lacking in what you are expressing. *Would* is like the word *but*; when you say 'but' in the beginning of your sentence, it becomes a nontruth. Here's an example, 'I like that dress, but…' Or 'I would go…but…' Make sense to you, Meems?"

You know, actually it did. I never paid attention to the words we use before like this and it's pretty cool. I nod my head.

"Okay, let's keep going," Bitsy says. "Look at the size of the word *happy*! It's purple, that's great. It means there will be a deep happiness surrounding you and it will be of and from the highest energies. You will also be surrounded by great strength of character that you will be able to depend on," she says as she points to the blue card. "The wavy lines mean you will question the dependability you seek in one moment and then you will know that it is there in the next. This is about learning to trust *you*. Trust that you are an old soul and there are many answers within that you haven't tapped into yet. They are waiting for the questions to come about.

"Remember," she says, moving on to the next card, "there is always magic in your heart. Again, trust, trust, trust! The last two words are about a time of healing, growth, caring, and moving forward. Once again, I see this as a very spiritual time of growth and allowing your heart to remain open because you are able to trust yourself.

"Now!" Bitsy exclaims. "Let's summarize. You, my dear, are extremely gifted, intuitive, and an old soul. When a challenge comes your way, you have the tools to overcome, prevail, and succeed. Whatever the task, event, or hurdle, you're capable of handling it physically, emotionally, and most especially, spiritually. So, tell me, with all this amazing energy at your beck and call, why are you so frightened and why don't you trust yourself?"

Oh geesh, here it is. How'd she know? I thought I really hid it well that I'm scared almost all the time. Scared I'm going to end up all alone. My parents are gone and there are no brothers or sisters, no cousins, just Gran. And, according to the doctors, she's really sick, so how much longer does she have, do I have? Of course I'm scared. And I'm supposed to trust myself with what? How?

I start to cry. *That's just great. Way to go, Meems. Show how strong you are!*

She takes my hands into hers and says, "Let the tears flow. They are salty to cleanse."

I ask how she knows the things she's told me.

Bitsy says, "I feel and see it in your auric energy field using pure clairvoyance, or clear vision. You know how your gran just seems to know things? She uses her intuition, listens to her heart and trusts the 'knowing' she has deep inside."

"Yeah," I answer, "that's Gran. What do I know?"

"Oh, my dear, you know more than you have ever dreamed possible. You simply need to begin to learn how powerful you truly are. That is why we have The Nook. We begin with meditation classes and go all the way to the highest philosophies. It is time for you to begin your studies, to open yourself to the fact that there is so much more to 'see' in this world than our three dimensional eyes allow for."

Bitsy shows me a calendar jam-packed full of classes. She says, "Look it over and tell me what grabs you. Listen for your inner voice. Trust yourself."

The one titled Beginner Psychic, Intuitive Development catches my eye first. The description says, "Are you curious about psychic development and working with your spirit guides?" My spirit what? Then it says, "Learn the magic of meeting and working with your spirit guides."

Bitsy is looking at me with a grin as wide as the ocean as my face turns bright red. The heaviness in my chest has lifted and my tears have dried. She simply nods and tells me which Monday mornings and evenings this class is held.

"Good choice," she whispers. "See how easy it is to hear the whispers of your wisdom?"

I'm feeling excited and looking forward to something for the first time in a very long time. Really looking forward!

Suddenly her timer dings: the reading is finished. It feels weird as I realize I had forgotten we were sitting in a busy event center with tons of people all around us. I think she took me off the earth plane with her. Somewhere I haven't been before! It was like the room disappeared and we were alone. There really is something to this woo-woo stuff.

Bitsy asks if I have any questions. Any questions? Is she kidding? Only about 1,000 and I've yet to process all she said, all she knew, how she knew it. Then she smiles and says, "We are doing a special meditation at four this afternoon. If you and Gran are still here, please come and experience it. It would be a great way to begin your meditation practice, which, young lady, you need to do every day! We tell our students at The Nook, twenty minutes in twenty-four hours…easy-peasy!" I ask if I can text or email with the questions I have as they surface. "Of course," she answers.

8

Meditation Is Cool

I grab Gran, who just sat down at the food court with an iced tea, and start to regurgitate all that just happened with lots of side comments as well. She just smiles and nods her head. I ask if we can stay for the meditation—it's only like an hour away. With a deep breath, Gran says, "Why not!" I'm all over it! We both use these moments to catch our breath.

We make our way to the lower floors of the hall and find room seven, where Artie and Bitsy are going to conduct the meditation. The room is completely full. We have to look around to find two seats together. Artie and Bitsy arrive and make their way to the front of the room. As the group noise subsides, we settle into our seats. I sense Gran is fading; she looks tired. Still, she smiles and pats me on the hand before looking forward. For a moment she leaves her hand on mine, connected.

Artie and Bitsy introduce themselves to the crowded room and talk about The Nook. They explain it's a place of meditation, mastering and learning ancient philosophies through classes and workshops, a place of support as a spiritual family, and a school of mysticism, metaphysics, and spiritual healing. They talk about who they are and what they do and how long they've done it, and they go back and forth speaking like a deftly hit ping-pong ball. Where one leaves off, the other picks up, and they are funny. I love these ladies! They dim the lights, instruct everyone to get as comfortable as possible and tell us to take three slow, deep, cleansing breaths, and as we do, we close our eyes.

Okay, so this is my first public meditation. I do sit quietly every now and then in my bedroom, but, you know, I don't actually turn off the chatter in my head. So, we'll see what happens here. My chin is down so I can look all around as covertly as possible. Are all these people really going to go deeply into the image we're about to be given? Can I? Gran's eyes are already closed and she looks as though she's so relaxed, she's asleep. Oh well, here goes, breathing slowly and deeply.

"And so, we begin with three deep, gentle, cleansing breaths. Relax your body, starting with your feet. Feel the energy of Mother Earth and the earth-star chakra coming in through the bottoms of your feet. Allow this relaxing, warm feeling to come up through your lower legs, over your knees and into your thighs; continue to bring the energy up over your hips and feel how soft and relaxed your lower body has become. Now, continue to draw the energy through the center of your body all the way up to your shoulders and down over your arms to your finger-tips, and allow the feeling of warm fullness to pool in the center of the palm of each hand. Now return your focus to your shoulders and draw the energy up through your throat and over your head. Shoot the energy out the very top of your head, your crown chakra, and allow it to shower softly, like a gentle rain, down, over your body back to the earth-star chakra. You are all doing a good job.

"Return to your third eye in the center of your fore-head, and as it slowly opens imagine yourself walking down a white gravel driveway toward a charming hotel. Look up at this old beauty. There are seven white marble steps that lead to a lovely wraparound porch upon which are many antique white rocking chairs. As you ascend the white marble steps you see two bright red two-story doors, the entrance to the hotel. Go to the doors and open one and step into the foyer of this amazing lodging. In the center of the foyer overhead is a magnificent crystal chandelier. The domed roof above it brings natural light to the crystals, and the foyer is abundant with rainbow colors swirling from the chandelier. Directly across the foyer from the entry is a long hallway. Cross the white marble floor to the hallway. Absorb the rainbow colors. As you get to the hallway, look down at the carpet. You will notice it is the plushest carpet you have ever seen; the color of the sky at midnight—a deep, velvet blue. Walk down the hall. At the end you will see an elevator. When you arrive, press the button marked with an arrow pointing upward. As the door slides open, step into the elevator. Directly ahead is another up arrow. Walk up to the button and press it. The doors behind you slide silently closed and you begin to slowly ascend. Listen to the floor count.

"One, feel yourself feeling lighter as you pass each floor. Two, you continue to become feather-like, your physical body fading away. Three, you are very light now and doing a great job. Four, you barely feel the weight of your physicality. Five, you arrive at the hotel garden, the doors of the elevator slide open, and you step out into the most beautiful garden you've ever seen. It is filled with colors and scents, exotic, bursting with the vibration of life. Breathe in the sweet aromas as you walk through the garden. Ahead you will notice a path that leads into an old forest. The trees are massive, reaching toward the sky. They are filled with leaves in all shades of green, from deep, dark forest green to light as the color of grass green. They cause the sun to shine down on the path in rays like layered star beams, showers from heaven. As the dappled light cascades all around you,

you continue on the path, seeing ahead a circle of marble benches. Keep moving toward them. The benches are all pure, white marble creating a circle surrounding a pure white tri-layered water fountain. Flowing over the edge of each level of the fountain is the clearest, cleanest water you'll ever see. Choose a bench to sit on and look toward the path from which you just entered the circle. Coming toward you is a being of light with the gentle outline of a human form. This being is your doctor of healing spirit guide. He or she is with you now to help whatever in your body needs support, extra energy, repairing, or healing. Take this time to sit in silence with your healing guide; direct your inner light to shine in all its fullness. We now enter a period of silence.

"And now you're back, feeling the weight and fullness of your physical body, here at the expo. We hope your meditation was peace-filled and brought to you what you needed."

What? I just closed my eyes. How could they be saying it's finished?

Gran touches my hand and says, "Sweetie, it's time to head home." I may be truly relaxed, but I'm very tired. She looks positively rejuvenated. "Are *you* ready to go, Meems?"

I nod affirmatively. I seem unable to speak at the moment. As we head to the exit, I feel a pair of eyes following me. As I turn, I see Bitsy watching me with a smile on her face. We wave to each other. I have this feeling we'll meet again soon.

For now, I need to focus on driving and let go of any thoughts I have of my experiences today. Traffic is heavy; it's like everybody is trying to leave at the same moment! I'll have time later to go over every little and big thing. I'll listen to the reading I recorded on my smartphone, and I need to review the time spent in the guided meditation. I'm seeing this movie in my mind and I think it's what happened in the meditation. I can't wait to get home.

9

Galen of Pergamum

I've got Gran settled into her bed, with a cup of her favorite passionflower green tea. She says it helps her rest like no other. Time to go to my safe spot, wrapped in my sweet, silky comforter, and see what I actually experienced. With my diary open and my favorite pencil in hand, I'm ready to relive the meditation. I'll listen to the reading later. Then I'll add notes from that to my diary too.

We began with instructions to relax our body. I did it. I felt my feet connecting to Mother Earth and energy like I never felt before began to buzz lightly in my feet. Focused on that, I was able to bring that energy up through my body. Throughout my whole being, I drew a tingling sensation all the way to my fingers. The palms of my hands became so hot. Whoa! The warmth spread all the way to the top of my head. It really did feel like a warm, gentle rain. I see the old hotel. I'm impressed. I'm also thinking and peeking around at those here in the convention hall lecture room. I need to stop, so I rerun the energy!

I believe I walked up the marble steps, no, more like floated. I'm looking up at the brightest red doors I've ever seen. The rocking chairs on the porch have a glow about them. I open the door. Being so huge I thought it would be heavy. It was lighter than the meringue on a lemon pie. The place is a kaleidoscope of colors swirling, circling, and bouncing off the white marble floors and walls. The dome above is shining light in a pale yellow, citrine color. I pause to feel the warm glow and it surrounds me. I head to the long hallway, which is lined with the thickest, deeply dark, royal blue carpet ever. I can feel the softness beneath my feet as I move down the hall. I see the elevator up ahead. The call button has a golden glow. I move to press it. It lights up before my finger even touches it. I enter the elevator and am instantly surrounded by a golden luminosity and a feeling of lightness. I am rising or floating or something! My body seems to be evolving into simple particles. When the elevator doors open, I glide out into a garden of nature's delights. There are brilliant hues of every color in the spectrum. The air is fresh and pure, replete with a myriad of fragrances. I'm blown away. The darkness of many trees gathered closely together shadows the path I follow. There is just enough light coming through the trees to ease my way forward and provide a safe feeling on the trail. I arrive at the white benches and look up at the water fountain that vibrates with life. Somehow, I know this water is the best of life.

I get comfortable on the third bench on the left. Just as I settle myself in, a large presence hovers in front of me. It's a man dressed in flowing white and gold robes. He's really tall. He nods to me in greeting and holds out his hand, indicating the space next to me on the bench. I nod back. Once he's seated, he speaks without moving his mouth, yet I hear him clear as day.

"I am Galen of Pergamum. I am your doctor of healing spirit guide. Together we will work on your health, be it physical, mental, emotional, or spiritual. We have come together by agreement. I have watched over you from the moment you took your first breath."

He looks into my eyes. Again, his lips aren't moving, yet I know everything he's saying. Once more, I hear his melodious voice.

"All you need to do, Meems, now that we've connected, is ask for me to come and be with you. I can watch over you, but I cannot help you if you don't ask. This is one of the rules of the universe. Do you understand?"

I do. I don't understand, but I feel as though I've known

Galen all my life. I suppose in a way I have! His energy envelops mine and together we sit in complete silence. There's not a thought in my head. There is, though, a warm, gentle buzzing through my body.

So, that was my first guided meditation. Within the silence I actually became totally still. No sound, no thoughts, no color, nothing. Just a slight shiver running through me, yet not me; I was just particles, not whole, not weighted, not solid. Next thing I know, we're being "called" back and it's time to leave. Yet I remember so much.

I have to know how that happened. Where'd I go? Did everybody in that room today go somewhere else? As I sit on my bed, knees tucked up under my chin, I feel safe, but at the same time I feel really freaked. Bitsy gave me her card. It's in my pocket poking me. Isn't that interesting! She said I could get in touch with her anytime about anything. She also said it was time for me to dedicate myself to studying, expanding, exploring, discovering, and raising my consciousness. All the classes I need are being held at The Nook, a thirty-minute drive from the house. I brought their calendar home with me. Now where'd I put it?

10

Besties

It's time for you to meet my two best friends. Alexandria (we call her Lexi) is five feet eight inches tall, blonde, and right out of the modeling magazine for Greco-Roman goddesses. Thing is, she's also really nice. She doesn't lord it over anybody that she's gorgeous, smart (4.0 average with AP classes), and captain of our high school cheerleading squad. Next, there's Jasmine. She's five feet tall and five-three in her highest heels, shoes she can't walk in to save her soul. Round everywhere is a good way to describe Jazzy's shape. Everything from her head to her toes is curvy, including the curly espresso-brown hair on her head. She has the most devastating petrified-wood brown eyes ever. Sometimes when you look into her eyes you see flashes of red and copper in the depth of the color. Sometimes they are a deep brown.

So, there you have our three musketeer-ettes. We've been friends since kindergarten. Oh, you want to know what I look like. Well, I'm right in the middle of Goddess Blonde and Espresso Round. I'm five foot four inches tall, with wavy light-brown and strawberry blond hair. Average weight, killer calves. I'm a Sagittarius, so I have great legs. Anyway, we all clicked way back in kindergarten and even when we had different teachers, like in the fifth grade when I got stuck with Mrs. Harrington and Jazzy and Lexi did not, we remained close. Mrs. Harrington had more dark body hair than any female in our school, or maybe on the planet. The kids called her Mrs. Hairy-Ton. Nice lady, boring teacher. Talked more about her appliances at home than she did the fractions we were supposed to be learning.

Every recess and lunch period we three girls always found each other and shared lunch and snacks. To this day we share our thoughts, feelings, and stories. It feels good to have somebody to talk with who understands and listens. Jazzy's parents are lawyers with a very busy practice, so Jazzy has to watch her little brother a lot and complains what a pest he is. He's actually the really good-looking side of Jazzy. He has her beautiful coloring and a very long, slender swimmer's body. Secretly, she really likes her brother and his mischievous sense of drama. Sometimes I think she feels more like his mother than his sister, after all she's had to watch over him since he was born. Jazzy was four when Jordan arrived. Seems like circumstances made us grow up fast! Now that we're all getting to the age where we're expected to act like adults, we get to be giggling girls when it's just us.

I haven't told Lexi and Jazzy about Gran's cancer. Every time I think I'm ready my throat closes. I know it's time; I need to share this burden so I can be strong and have plenty of love space for Gran as she goes deeper into this challenging journey.

11

Hello, Hermes

Gran is away for the day with her lady friends so Lexi, Jazzy, and I have the house to ourselves. I told them all about my day at the expo, how Bitsy and Artie knew so many personal details, how freaked I was that they knew so much, and of course that I want to study with them. I'm thinking maybe I can get them to come to The Nook with me.

Here we are gathered in my beautiful safe-haven room and we three have decided to repeat the meditation I learned at the expo. We get cozy with my comforter and some extra blankets so we each have something warm and safe cocooning us, then we begin by relaxing into our bodies.

I whisper that we need to connect to Mother Earth and as I do, once again I'm all abuzz! We each draw energy up through our bodies starting at our feet and going all the way to the very tops of our heads. I can feel the heat of that energy blazing through me. I hope Lexi and Jazzy can too. We climb up the white marble steps to the old hotel and open the giant red door. As before, the area is filled with twirling, shimmering rainbow colors.

I know I'm no longer in the third dimension; I'm not walking but floating down the carpeted hall to the elevators. I enter the garden and head to the path through the trees and suddenly I'm not alone. I get this eerie feeling of a hand on my right arm, and without moving my head, I move my eyeballs as far to the right as they will go and peek at what's next to me.

A deep voice chuckles and says, "Welcome little one."

Oh geesh. I'm really not alone. I become frozen in place; I can't move, float, or glide, so I make myself turn my head. I feel like an owl, nothing but my head swiveling! Standing next to me is the most muscular guy I've ever seen. My eyes go from his head to his feet, taking him all in as slowly as I can. His hair is glowing golden, and he's dressed really weird with wings at his ankles and on his hat. Am I seeing my first angel? This is so freaky! His clothing looks like a small dress, sort of a Roman-style mini-tunic. In his right hand he holds a staff that has a caduceus at the top, and woven around the body of the staff is what looks like two snakes intertwined. Snakes scare me. I can feel my energy changing to something heavy. He can feel it too.

"You are safe with me, little one. I am Hermes and I am your Doctor of Philosophy, the spirit guide that is your teacher. Will you sit on the white bench at the water fountain with me?"

OMG, what do I do now? Okay, Meems, get a grip!

"Sure," I think but don't say, and we float over to a white marble bench on the other side of the fabulous fountain. I can't seem to find my tongue, although if I did it would probably be hanging out because he is so gorgeous. Guess I better go home and google Hermes. I'm thinking he's like a Greek god.

He takes my hands in his. His are big, warm, and a little rough. I am instantly calm. He lays his staff down on the bench and I no longer feel afraid of snakes, of anything.

"Sooo, what are we doing here? I'm supposed to be meditating," I say.

He looks into me, really deep, into the inner me that other than Gran I almost never let anyone see. "I am here to guide your spiritual lessons. It is time for you to rise beyond your earthly self and claim as yours the power of source that has been yours for eternity. You are not separate from anything or anyone in this entire universe, and you need to begin the journey of learning this. Call on me whenever you have doubts as to which direction to go or what to do. I will help, though you must call on me first. Remember, you must ask for help."

My head is nodding up and down like a bobblehead doll. Suddenly I realize I'm no longer physical, I have no body. I am pure energy.

"This, little one, is your body of light. You hold in this body all your wisdom, the knowledge of your sacred contract, your connection to the Akashic Records, to the ancients, to all that is. It is the true essence of your being. I will leave you now. Dwell in this energy for a while before you return to your normal way and your friends. Be at peace, little one."

And just like that, poof, he's gone. So, I stay where I am. Oh my, that gave me quite an electrifying jolt, *I am*. Yes, somehow, I know that *I am*. And that saying those words elevates me, raises my vibrations, takes me to a higher place where I can be my highest self. How can I live in the world and yet be at this higher energy level?

Abruptly I feel a tap on my knee and hear, "Are you in there, Meems? Yoo-hoo, where'd you go? We're tired of sitting here."

And that fact I'm returned to my room, sitting cross-legged on my comforter with Jazzy and Lexi staring at me like I've grown an extra nose or something. "Why are you looking at me like that?" I ask.

"Umm, we both heard a sharp intake of breath and opened our eyes and you were glowing, like you were on a stage lit up by the footlights. We were really relaxed, guess that was meditation, and then whoosh and we're wide awake and you're translucent. That's totally too weird, Meems."

Of course, that was Jazzy's take. Lexi was just sitting in my room, wrapped tightly in her blanket, staring at me. She finally shook her head side to side and said, "Meems, all that stuff you told us about other planes of existence and other beings is true? Did you just leave your body?"

Sheepishly, I grinned and said, "Yeah, I did. It's got to be true." So, they asked me to spill and I did. I told them all about Hermes and his staff of snakes and his golden looks and his winged hat and shoes. I explained how we spoke to each other except as I did, I realized we never said a word. Not a syllable was uttered; we did it all in our minds. I'm not sure if I should be freaked, or smugly satisfied. Smugly satisfied is where I'm leaning.

Jazzy jumped up, folded her blanket, and barked orders to me and Lexi. "Time for an ice cream cone. Get your bikes out and we're off to Cone Palace. I read somewhere when you do psychic work, it depletes the sugar in your body. Meems was way out there, so she needs some sugar."

And off we went. I knew I'd return to my visit with Hermes when I got home. I couldn't push these girls too hard first time out of the gate!

12

Mom

I have my window wide open tonight; I need the energy of the moon shining in on me as I lie in bed. It feels both comforting and empowering. Life has been taking a lot of crazy turns lately and I'm not sure I'm ready. I'm not sure I'm not. What will all the spiritual growth really feel like? What would happen if I left my body and didn't come back? Will I change so much no one will recognize me? Maybe Artie and Bitsy would know. I'll ask Gran if we can check out The Nook this week. Suddenly I'm so tired I can't keep my eyes open.

"Meems," a voice whispers. "Meems, honey, it's me."

"Mom, is that you?"

"Yes, dear, I'm here. I'm always here."

I'm instantly awake. No, I'm not. I'm dreaming. No, I'm not. My mother is here with me. She looks the same, just a little luminous. She sits down of the edge of my bed and rubs her hand in little circles on my comforter.

"This reminds me of rainbow fluorite. My favorite stone! And it's so soft, so silky. Without your dad and me being around, you needed a soft place to fall, a place upon which you could land and feel safe. Gran has certainly been a trouper, and I might add, has done a great job of loving you. You are a fine young woman. I'm very proud of you."

I can't believe she's actually here. What do I say?

"Where have you been, and why has it taken you so long to come to me? Where's Dad? Why are you here now?" Then I cross my arms over my chest and pout. Okay, so, not so grown up right this minute. I've waited a long time for this moment and certainly wasn't expecting it to happen out of the blue. Where was my mother all those times I looked at the stars in the sky, as Gran instructed, and begged her to come back to me?

"Oh, my sweet baby, I know how difficult this has been for you." Actually, she has no clue! "I had to wait until you were ready and there was a period of your time on Earth where the healing of our energetic bodies had to take place. The accident that took us from you was quite devastating to our physical bodies and because of that our auric fields were in tatters. There is so much for us to share, so much for you to become open to. Even with no time existing where we are now, we have to be aware that time does exist on Earth."

Whoa, what? No time? Time isn't real? How could there be no time except here on Earth? There's so much I don't know. Should I tell my mom how much I miss her and Dad? Does she already know? Can she read my mind? If she can, does she know how long I was mad at them? Does she know I still get pretty angry at the cards we were all dealt? Do I have to watch all my thoughts now? Does she know how freaked I am right this minute?

"Meems, I will return from time to time to chat in this way. If you need me, you simply need to think about me. I'll feel your energy and come to you. There is, my sweet girl, so very much for you to discover. We ask that you take baby steps. The energies can be a bit overwhelming at first. We love you, darling. Good night." And poof, just like my spirit guide, Mom's gone.

"Wait!" I scream. "Wait!"

Gran knocks softly on my door and asks if I'm alright. I was just screaming at a ghost, and now I'm crying, so I'm not sure how to answer. I'm dazed, flustered, surprised, scared, and freaked. No, I'm not alright!

I open my door and collapse into her waiting arms, sobbing. She gently guides me to my bed and we sink into my comforter. As Gran rocks me in her arms, I cry as I haven't in a long time. Then, when it seems I have no more tears, Gran takes me by the shoulders, and holding me at arm's length says, "She came, didn't she?" It isn't so much of a question as it is a statement. "I thought I felt her energies! I wish she had stayed until I could see her too. Oh, this time thing is such a nuisance! Do tell me all about your visit!"

Wait a minute. This time thing is a nuisance? Ugh!

So, I told her about the moon warming me, about Mom popping in and out, and about how frustrated I felt. Gran simply held my hand and nodded with a quirky grin on her face.

The next day I told Lexi and Jazzy. They didn't nod, or grin. I could feel them trying to make space between us without really moving. Oh, I should have kept quiet. When Gran and I started this journey by going to the expo, I was afraid of this very thing. Though we three have been through thick and thin together, I think this journey will be too much for them and we will become less and less connected. I don't want to lose my best friends, and I don't want to stop pursuing this new aspect of life I've just begun to discover. What am I to do?

13

Sacred Contracts

Spring break is just about over and it's back to school. I've been really busy working at the law office so I can put some money away and haven't spoken with Lexi and Jazzy since I called them over to tell them about the visit from my mother, which hasn't happened again. I hope they're not avoiding me I'm not sure I could take that.

Gran is back on her routine of chemo. One week of meds, one week off, for the next eight weeks, and this routine will take us to the end of the school year, finals, and a week after exams, graduation. I feel like time is going too quickly. Mom basically said it was an illusion. If it is, why can't I slow it down? If I had the power to do anything I wanted, first thing I would do would be to take Gran's cancer away. Gran says that Mom and Dad leaving, us being a team, and her illness is all a part of our sacred contracts. The calendar for The Nook said they were teaching a class about those contracts. Since I don't have school tomorrow, I think I'll go and learn about sacred contracts!

*   *   *

Evening classes begin at six thirty. Gran was too tired to go so I drove by myself to The Nook at a beautiful spot in New Hope. Nestled in the quaint, riverside shopping district of New Hope that draws thousands of tourists, The Nook is like an oasis away from the stores and the shoppers. Located on a tree-lined street with the Delaware River flowing serenely by the back porch, The Nook is in a sweet old house right next to the famous 1740 House. The 1740 is an old country home turned into a restaurant, club, and all around go-to spot. You can almost feel the spirits of history inhabiting the street. I fell in love with this place the moment I saw it.

Tonight, I'm greeted by a lady about my gran's age and instantly feel welcome in the warm foam-blue, sand, and soft gray colors of the space. There's a little store for stones, incense, books, handmade jewelry, and candles. I'm drawn to the amethyst geodes shining a deep purple in the light of the entry to the NookStore. I'm glad to have the store space to kind of hide in as people come in the door greeting each other with warm, caring hugs. My gran would love this place!

Bitsy comes in and hugs every one of us and knows each person by name, including me. She whispers in my ear that she's thrilled to see me. I'm shocked she would remember me after just one meeting! The class passes so fast I can't believe ninety minutes are gone. What I learned I will slowly digest. Gran is right about the contracts. She's right about a lot of things. I can't wait to tell her all about the class, the people here at The Nook, and the gorgeous stuff in the NookStore.

*   *   *

I'm home in twenty minutes and Gran has my favorite homemade hot chocolate waiting for me. I can see she feels a little better. Her color isn't so pale and her eyes have some twinkle in them. She takes my hand, sits me in my favorite chair, which she has pulled up to her favorite chair, and says, "Tell me, Meems, tell me all about The Nook, the class, and the people. Make sure I get all the juicy details!"

I take a sip of the cocoa, roll it all around my mouth, savoring the thick, delicious chocolate as only Gran can make it, and begin my story. First, I describe The Nook, its location, and colors, then I tell her about all the goodies I want from the NookStore. Then I get down to business in describing the class.

"Our energy origins are in the divine, the source of our sacred contract. With divine guidance—because we are divine!—we cocreate the contract and fill it with the lessons we come to earth to learn. We are meant to have all of our relationships, Gran, all of them! Parents, close friends, our own children, are meant to be, even our opponents, mean girls, jerky guys, and adversaries. You're so right about so many things, Gran! I can't believe it!"

Now I'm thinking as I sip my dark, sweet drink that means Lexi and Jazzy are meant to be in my life and they will each bring me some kind of lesson as I will bring something to them. I sure hope the lessons we created with each other are mild, not harsh, you know like only loving. Though I know they loved me, the lessons from my parents weren't so gentle, not even close; they turned out to be bone-crushingly tough, that's for sure. It still hurts me to think about the night of their accident. If it still hurts so much, maybe I don't have the lesson yet. Wow, where'd that thought pop up from? Anyway, back to my story. I'm starting to get that it's all about our spiritual growth! Go figure.

"Gran, every relationship and experience is an opportunity to grow and transform. Some relationships offer multiple opportunities and in each we get to choose how to react, how to exercise our own power. And every contractual connection carries a piece of your spirit in it. That means for those close to me, there's a piece of my spirit in them and them in me.

"In all of this I'm realizing that we embody the laws of the universe every time we exercise our power of choice! Learning all this makes me feel somehow bigger. Yeah, the word is *bigger*. Oh, Gran, it makes so much sense to me. I'm going to call Lexi and Jazzy and invite them over so we can talk about that night we had a visit from Mom and get any 'ghosts' out of the way before school starts. I know they were totally freaked!"

I'm going to ask Gran if I can join The Nook's spiritual fitness membership so I can go to class anytime I want. I'm eager to learn more. It just feels so right! And, I can get a student membership, so it won't break the bank!

14

Morning Star

Lexi and Jazzy came over the next morning. We hugged and they seemed almost contrite, definitely on the guilty side. I told them all about what I learned about our sacred contracts and how special they are to me. They explained that the meditation really scared them because while they were watching me, I seemed to transform and maybe even not be in the room with them anymore. Afterward, they didn't know what to say, so they didn't say anything and decided they would just stay away. They both felt ashamed. As we held hands, I told them there was nothing to feel ashamed about. How could they understand what was happening when I barely understood? They decided they will come to classes at The Nook with me and explore as I explore.

Now I'm really revved and very relieved. I decide I was right in the first place when I said nothing could tear the three of us apart, so, I told them about Gran's health. Then we all cried. It felt good not to feel alone in my worry about Gran and about where my life could be headed. I made them promise not to tell anyone else, especially their parents. If they told, then their parents would pick up the phone and offer Gran whatever help she may need and Gran would want to clobber me. I guess it's her story to tell others, not mine. We looked over The Nook calendar and we three muskateer-ettes decided we're all going to try out a beginner psychic development class Monday night. I'm looking forward to learning how to use my gifts (that's what Gran calls them), and having my two best friends with me makes it really special and maybe not so intimidating.

*   *   *

Here we are, Monday night at The Nook with the lights turned down low. The teacher is Lesley, a certified medium. Lesley tells us all about her metaphysical journey and how she started out as a nonbeliever. There's the three of us, two ladies in their forties, and a giant of a man with a very long beard. I'm wondering what's up, as the energies here feel really spooky, like there are others in the room we can't see.

The energies give me the shivers. Jazzy is wrapped in a blanket and Lexi is wearing her straightest posture, a sure sign she feels something too. The class begins with the circle of protection prayer, and a talk about our spirit guides. We are each given a packet that explains the five guides we are supposed to meet in this class and the protocols of proper conduct when working with our guides and being in the astral plane.

Whoa! I keep quiet about having met a couple of these guides already.

After an explanation of each spirit guide and their job with us and the step-by-step process for giving a message to someone other than ourselves, we are each called one at a time to the front of the room where Lesley takes our hands in hers, has us take three deep, slow, gentle breaths and close our eyes. She directs us to focus on our third eye in the middle of the forehead, making sure it's open and in that space, we look down at our feet. We're instructed to look for feet in front of ours. I see sweet, pudgy, bare little girl feet. I've got to be making this up, right? This *is* my imagination, right? Of course, not, right? Haven't I been through this already?

Then Lesley says she sees chubby little feet there and that they belong to my joy guide. She encourages me to keep going, to look at her clothes and describe them. I see a ruffled, sparkly, silver-blue dress and a blue hairband with a big shiny star twinkling in the little one's hair. My heart is thumping wildly in my chest. I keep my eyes closed as Lesley has told me to do, mostly because I'm afraid if I open them everyone will be staring at me and this will all just disappear. Lesley tells me to introduce myself and ask the little one what her name is—out loud.

Ugh. Okay, here goes. Which name should I use? I decide in a flash I'll use the name everyone else uses. "Um, hi, I'm Meems." That's all I could think to say. "Um, what is your name, please?"

And then I hear a sweet sound in my head, like little chimes tinkling in a breeze, and I suddenly know her name is Morning Star. I can no longer keep my eyes closed; they pop open and I look directly into Lesley's grinning face. She tells me what a great job I've done meeting my joy guide and that all week I need to sit quietly in meditation and spend time finding out all I can about Morning Star. I need to get to know her by asking her what her favorite flower is and her favorite color and why we're together this lifetime. Then Lesley tells me it's time to go to work by giving someone in the room a message from Morning Star. Maybe I could just go sit down instead. Lesley isn't letting go of my hand! I look at Lexi and Jazzy, who haven't done this yet, and their eyes are as big as the clocks on the high school wall. What have I got to lose if I say yes? I nod my head up and down.

She says, "Okay, close your eyes again, call Morning Star in by introducing yourself and her, which tells her it's time to go to work." Then, as instructed, I walk around the room holding out my dominant hand, aiming it at each person as I walk by. I feel really uncomfortable staring at everyone. She says I will know which person is to receive the message by a tug in their direction, sparkles over their head, or my hand will get really hot or cold or begin to tingle. As I walk toward the man with the beard, whose name is Devon, my hand seems to catch fire. I look to Lesley and she nods her head at me. She knows it's him. She knows!

I take a deep breath to calm my jitters and ask if he'd like a message from my joy guide, Morning Star.

In a beautifully deep voice he answers, "Absolutely!"

I panic. My whole body feels frozen. Then I feel Lesley step up next to me, place her hand on the small of my back, and whisper, "You've got this. Simply take a breath and listen for the message."

I close my eyes again and hear the sweet chimes inside and then this super-text message floats into my thoughts. I tell Devon, "When one life ends, another begins, though you may not always get to know when or where." Okay, this is so outer limits!

I am freaked out and afraid to say another word. Then Lesley instructs that I may ask if the message made sense.

"Oh, yes," Devon answers. "We recently had a death in our family. My eighteen-year-old nephew died in a car accident, and I'm questioning everything."

Oh boy, oh boy, oh boy. I can't even look at Jazzy and Lexi! What have I tapped into, what have we all tapped into? After closing the heart bridge that helped me unite with Devon, I finally get to sit down. That night everyone is able to pass on information to the intended recipient Even Lexi and Jazzy! What a night for us all! The ride home is pretty much quiet, as we are all lost in thoughts of what just happened, what we are capable of doing, and where we are skilled enough to go.

15

The Gate Keeper

The next day I can't wait to get myself all set up for meditation. I read my packet from class last night and think about Galen and Hermes. I must, absolutely must, connect again with Morning Star. Finally, after dinner, with Gran all settled in for the night, I light my favorite lavender candle, plump up all my pillows, and settle in with my best lotus position. Well, it's really one leg crossed over the other. My twist-into-a-pretzel exercise days feel like they're long gone, never to see sunlight again. Ha! I did give yoga a try. It wasn't for me. I thought I would fall asleep in each class.

Okay, time for me to settle in and breathe. I take three deep, cleansing breaths, relax my body, shush my monkey-chatter mind (well, most of it), run the energy of Mother Earth through my body, and open my third eye. In my mind's eye, I see my favorite walking trail. My go-to place is through a woody trail that rolls up and down like a junior-sized rollercoaster. I like the way the sun dapples through the trees and makes the leaves all sparkly in so many richly abundant shades of green I can't count them. I usually feel like the rays of sun are my dad's hands, reaching down to touch the top of my head as I hike. At the end of the trail is a small waterfall. It's not breathtaking or anything like that, like Victoria Falls in South Africa; it's a gentle spray over a cliff that used to be a part of local mountains that are so old, they are more like hills now.

I see all this in my mind and when I arrive at the falls, I get comfy and ask my joy guide, Morning Star, to come and sit with me. It can't be more than a moment when I hear bells tinkling. I wonder if it's the sound of the water slipping over the rocks and landing in a small pool at the base. Then I know it's her. I don't know how I know. I just do. We sit quietly side by side for a time. I don't know how long. And if I've moved outside the physical realm and there's no time here, then I suppose it doesn't matter. I feel so shy with Morning Star. I don't know where to start. So, I blurt out, without speaking of course, "Do you know my mom?"

Then I hear her. Not like everyday, normal hearing, but a gentle whisper inside my head with the sound of tinkling bells. "Yes, Meems, your mother and I are well acquainted. We are together often these days wondering when you will awaken. You are awakening now. We are all excited. As I am your gate keeper, it is I who will help you communicate more easily with your other spirit guides and your mother and father, and all that is."

I don't know what to say. It takes a long moment for me to interpret what she's said and absorb it. It's not like Morning Star is speaking another language or anything like that. It's just that I really can't believe I'm communicating with a spirit and it has to sink in!

Next, I ask, "Why do I hear tinkling bells when you come in?"

She lets me know she likes wearing a little necklace made of tiny silver bells all strung on gossamer threads. *Gossamer, really? Who uses a word like* gossamer? Then I feel a light cuff on my right hand. The spot is all of a sudden hot, like flaming hot. I think my joy guide just smacked me.

Oh, this is crazy, just crazy. No, I tell myself, not crazy, different. Lesley said I needed to learn to trust my intuition, my inner voice. Bitsy said the same thing at my reading. I know it's time to return from my meditation and my visit with Morning Star. I want to offer her a hug and just like that I feel a warm hug around my waist. I forgot she was a little girl. This working and communicating with spirit energies is going to take practice and getting used to. I feel myself walking away from the waterfalls and going back over the hills and valleys of my walking trail and then I'm back in my bed. Without opening my eyes, I stretch out my body and decide to stay in this restful, peaceful place for as long as I can without falling asleep.

16

The Path Changes

I've been back to The Nook so many times lately I can't even count. I go right after I finish up my filing job at the attorney's office. On top of returning for Psychic Development multiple times (enough to meet all but my master guide), I have studied Protection for the Light Worker, Sacred Geometry, Fibonacci and the Golden Ratio, Healing Meditation, Candle Magic, Sacred Contracts, Essential Oils, Herbs and Plants, The Art of Happiness Buddhist Meditation, Breath Work, Chiming Bowls and Sound, and Reading Palms. I would have never imagined there was so much to learn. When I read the Harry Potter series, I really didn't take all the magic stuff too seriously. Now I feel like Harry did when he first arrived at Hogwarts. I can't believe how much I don't know, never had a clue about, and how much there is to learn. When Artie told me that if I gave her thirty-five to forty years she would help me to be a great medium, she wasn't kidding! Every instructor at The Nook is a caring, knowledgeable, expansive person and so willing to share their insights and gems of learning!

Gran has been pretty steady with her chemo and not too sick, so life has settled into a fairly smooth routine. I'm inching my way toward graduation and a whole new world has opened up for me. Sometimes Lexi and Jazzy go with me to The Nook, other times I'm on my own. I am a NookSter member now, and they are not, so classes cost them allowance money.

Every now and then Gran comes with me to one of the multitude of meditations held there. I think it helps her health. At least she's not fading as I expected. When we met the breath teacher, we found out she is also very accomplished in the art of Reiki healing. Reiki is energy that comes through the practitioner from the universe and helps the body promote its own healing. Gran now has a weekly Reiki energy healing appointment with Moraine. She says she can feel the energies coming into her and ever since she started the appointments, she hasn't had the bad reactions to the chemo she originally had. Anything that helps Gran without adding extra medications thrills me. I'm not ready to let her go; I still need her in my life. I'll take every moment I can get. Gran is also taking Moraine's breath work class which is helping her to release the tension she's been holding on to since Mom and Dad died. Mom was, after all, Gran's daughter. I hadn't really thought about her loss before. I felt knocked out of my socks in breath class when Moraine mentioned to Gran that she needed to clear these energies in order to keep her healing journey going in an improving direction.

The girls and I get together at least two nights a week to share a meditation in my bedroom. Though Jazzy and Lexi haven't felt the magnetic draw to learning all about other planes of existence, other worlds, and other powers like I have, we still all benefit from sharing quiet time together. I get it now why they call silence sacred. After we sit in silence, Lexi and Jazzy and I study for tests and we are killing them with high marks. That alone makes it sacred. I learned how to use a pendulum in a divination class and how to quiet my mind so the answer I seek with my pendulum comes from my inner wisdom, from my soul. Of course, my pendulum is an amethyst. I love the beauty of the shades of purple sparkling in the facets of the stone. I'm going to take a stones and gems class this summer to get more information on the healing, calming, balancing power of the rocks and gemstones. That course will be taught by another powerhouse Reiki person who guides a potent healing meditation every month.

I've kept up my work at the law office and will continue to do so after graduation, but I want to spend as much time as I can at The Nook over the summer break. I decided that when fall comes I'll go to the local campus of Penn State rather than up to the main campus in Happy Valley. I'll be close to Gran that way and still able to "play" at The Nook.

17

The Hall of Knowledge

Graduation's next week. I can't believe it. Our school colors are gold and blue, so our caps and gowns are too. The gown is a bright gold with blue trim on the cuffs with a royal blue sash worn over the shoulder and across the front of the body. All of our club pins and award ribbons are attached to the sash. Lexi, Jazzy, and I are near the top of our class so we have a lot of decorations.

Now that exams are over, I can spend more time at The Nook. My meditations have been out of this world. Really, I mean out of this world! Sometimes I see other worlds in our universe, sometimes I find myself stepping into an antique, full-length mirror and visiting other lives. Some call other lives past lives. I have learned that all of our lifetimes are happening right now, we just see the one we see. Physics teaches us that there is no such thing as a straight line, so how can our lives have been lived on a straight timeline? If time is an illusion and doesn't exist anywhere else other than here on Earth, because we need it to stay organized, how can we not be living our lifetimes all at once? Anyway, I like to go and see these lives and who I am. We learned when going down the darkly carpeted hall in The Grand Hotel that the doors on both sides of the hall lead to new and exciting things and places. In one meditation at The Nook, we went into a beautiful ballroom and when we sat in the chair in the center of the room, we were transported to the Hall of Knowledge. I love the idea that we are eternal beings and when we "die" we're simply leaving our meat suits behind, becoming once again pure energy.

When I went to the Hall of Knowledge, I was able to communicate telepathically with the beings that were there. That was so cool. Every thought I had was acknowledged in a nonverbal communication with those around me. You can be sure I started watching my thoughts. When I was thinking, "I'm not sure I like not having words," a lovely, shimmering being of aqua-blue came right up to me and asked, "And why not? We all have words. Here we don't need to speak them. They simply are; just as we simply are. Take a look at yourself as you are now, simply energy. Perhaps then, you will understand how clear your thoughts and words truly are, or can be."

Then the color just floated away. Not a word was spoken; I heard all that in my head. Then when I went to look into the looking glass on the wall in the room I was in, all I saw was a pale pink form. Me, floating, shining, glowing with just an echo of a body, yet my body was gone. I didn't even have a head!

"Oh, chili beans," I thought. "I hope I get my body back. If I don't, Gran will be all alone. I won't graduate. I have to get back." And poof, I was back to my body. That particular meditation didn't go as others had, as I scared myself out of it. Now that is a very heavy, weighty feeling; it left me with a kind of a headache. The relaxation you're in disappears so fast, it leaves you feeling like lead weights are attached to your legs and to move you have to drag them around. I will have to work at not doing that anymore.

Bitsy told a class that working on a higher plane of existence needs to be studied with the right instructors so you are well protected and safe. There are tricksters "out there" and they may want to attach to you to come back into a body. I don't want to be attached to anybody I don't know, especially a trickster. I feel like if you didn't live your life to the fullest potential because of your choices, or get the lessons of your sacred contract, I'm not, absolutely *not*, giving you a vessel to trash again. Whoa, that's a bit judgey! Oh well! This is my body and my life, and even if it's not always easy, it's mine!

18

Running Bull

The moon is full tonight. I'm going to put my stones out in the moonlight to charge them. I wonder what will come tonight! I now own kyanite, malachite, amazonite, fluorite, moonstone, selenite, rose quartz, and lapis lazuli.

The moon looks really huge! I feel as though I could reach out and just touch it, hanging in the sky like a brand-new soccer ball ready to be caught. I've set up my pillows in the garden and placed my stones in a circle around me. I close my eyes, take my three deep breaths, and run the energy from Mother Earth through my body. The shadows in the garden seem to be moving.

"Meems," I hear a deep voice say. "Meems, it is time for us to get to know each other."

I can suddenly smell pipe tobacco. I know that voice. Why do I know that voice? Oh my goodness, it's my protector guide, Running Bull. I haven't spent any time with him since I met him in class at The Nook. Apparently, the time has come. Here goes…

"I'm listening."

"Look at the moon little one."

Geesh, why does everyone call me little one?

"Feel the moon, feel her power. Look into her light and absorb her energy deep into your core chakras. Open the central energy line of your being through your chakra centers and channel this opportunity to cleanse, empower, and heal yourself. The moon will guide you as you calm the deepest recesses of your mind. If you are frightened, the moon will heighten your fear; if you are happy and content, the full moon will enhance these feelings; if you are angry, your anger will intensify. Be aware that any emotion you are feeling when the moon is full will be significantly exaggerated. So, calm yourself; find peace of mind, body, and spirit as the moon expands to her fullest and most potent energies. She will share all of herself with you. It is up to you to do the work to absorb, learn, and be. Remember, the sun gives us our spirit and energy; the moon gives us our soul and emotions. Now we will sit together and practice sacred silence in the energies of our great sister of the sky."

My heart is racing; my breath is so shallow I'm getting dizzy. I need to do as Running Bull is saying, I need to be calm. This is blowing my mind, my mind that's now in the fourth dimension. Oh my God! I'm doing it, I'm doing it!

A deep resonant, vibration next to me says, "Shh, quiet your mind, little one. Seek your quiet space; turn off your inner chatter. Here it serves you not."

Okay, three deep breaths are really needed here. In through my nose, out through my mouth. Focus, focus, focus! As I breathe, I feel myself settling down. I release the fear that came over me when I first felt the presence of Running Bull. I *know* I have nothing to fear; still this is so new to me, and I *am* alone out here in the garden, you know, like people alone. Slowly I become still on the inside as well as the outside and then it happens.

I can feel the energy of the moon. *I can feel the energy of the moon.* It feels as though energy is pouring down through the top of my head, and like thick honey sliding down the side of a glass jar, the energy is flowing in slow motion down through the center of my body and along my spine. I let my eyes drift closed and totally surrender to the feelings.

I don't know how much time has passed when I feel a warm tingling on my hands, which are resting on my knees. I realize Running Bull is letting me know his energies are receding; my meditation in the moonlight is over. My body is buzzing, from head to toes. Is this what I want? Am I the one doing all this work, or am I being taken over? If I were a Harry Potter wizard, I'd have no problem believing it was possible to have a download directly from the moon. I'm not a wizard. Am I?

I gather up my circle of stones, place them in the leather medicine bag Gran bought for me at the expo, and slowly make my way back to the house. I don't want to lose any of the energies I'm currently feeling, so I take my time.

As I slide down under my covers, I hear a deep-voiced chuckle. "Meems, it is okay. You will not lose your moon charge. It is now a part of every cell in your body. We will talk again soon. You can expect to sleep well tonight, little one."

I hope Running Bull knows what he's talking about. I sure don't want to lose this feeling. How can he *not* know what he's talking about? What am I talking about? This is all so confusing! I have all these thoughts bouncing around my head; I know I'll never get to sleep tonight. Oh, it's going to be a long night! Then, like someone flipped a switch, I'm sound asleep.

19

The Panic Button Is Pressed

After a great all-the-way-through-the-night sleep I literally bounce down to the kitchen to tell Gran all about my moonlight meditation; except, she's not there. She's not in her usual spot filling our old 1950s percolator with fresh, ground coffee, with eggs cooking on the stove and bagels in the toaster. A body-freezing panic grabs a hold of me. I work to make myself breathe and not go tearing through the house in a total panic, though I'm not very far from it. I look first in her bedroom, not there. Then, I check all the bathrooms, not there. I look everywhere, but she's not anywhere.

Oh God, don't take her from me!

I'm back in the kitchen deciding if I should scream at the top of my lungs when out of the corner of my eye, I see a movement in the backyard. There she is, there she is!

I throw open the back door, pretty sure I'm about to throw up.

"Where have you been?" I yell at Gran as I charge into the garden. "Why are you sitting here in the dampness? What is wrong with you?" I shout all this before I realize all my fear has just poured out of my mouth.

Gran turns around and with one eyebrow raised gives me the "watch yourself, young lady" look.

I'm immediately contrite and feel terrible for having yelled at her. I sink to my knees in front of her and begin to cry. "I was so scared"—I hiccup— "I didn't know where you were or if something had happened to you. There was no food or coffee going in the kitchen. My heart stopped; I thought you had died in the night and I didn't even knoooow," I sobbed.

"And you're sitting here in your bathrobe without a sweater or anything to keep the morning chill off of you and you'll catch your death with a cold. How could you?" I continued to cry my eyes out as if I were connected to the garden hose with a never-ending supply of water!

Gran put her hand on my head and began to pat and stroke me as though I were a puppy. I needed her touch and didn't care in the moment that I was slobbering all over her like a little child. Eventually, my heart rate returned to normal and I took a deep breath.

"Child," she said, "I'm merely sitting in the garden. I

started out in the kitchen with the percolator in my hands and something, some unusual energy, drew me out into the fresh, crisp morning air. I didn't think about getting my shawl or a sweater. It was a powerful energy that gained my attention. I don't know why, but I never felt the morning chill. I got lost in the dew on the grass, in the sparkle of the flower petals so aglow in the early morning light. I sat here stroking my childhood cat that came for a visit. A beautiful Persian named Misty. She was a mixture of white and tan, a real glamour-puss. Oh, how she made me laugh. She had the sweetest face and the calmest personality of any cat I'd ever seen. I loved her so much and was tickled that she came in for a visit! I felt a peace in my heart I haven't known in a long time and I lost track of the time. I'm not at all cold. As a matter of fact, I'm delightfully warm all over!"

Gran was okay! *Whew, what a bullet we dodged.* Then it dawned on me that she had picked up the energies of the full moon I had attracted through my meditation and the energies of Running Bull. I had to be more mindful.

I took Gran's hands in mine as I rose from the ground and pulled her toward the warmth of the house. I settled her into her chair and made the coffee myself. I also cooked a pot of hearty oatmeal so she'd have something to stick to her ribs and I had something to do as I told my story of the full moon meditation with Running Bull.

At the end of our meal and my story, Gran took my hands in hers, gave me one of her brightest smiles, and said, "Oh, Meems, it's about time, my sweet girl! I knew you had extraordinary gifts. I also knew you had to discover them on your own."

20

Pomp and Circumstance

It's a beautiful May evening—graduation! The football stadium is decorated with the gold and blue that are the school colors. Ribbons of color float gently in the early evening breeze. I can't believe how many people are here. Gran was able to get a seat right up front, so she won't miss a thing. Graduating in the top ten of our class and the National Honor Society, Jazzy, Lexi, and I enter in the procession right behind the valedictorian and the class officers. A part of me is excited in an over-the-moon kind of way, and a part of me is extremely sad that my parents won't be here seated next to Gran.

We're all busy setting our sashes, adjusting our robes, and hugging each other. Some of the kids here have gone to school together since kindergarten. Now that's history! The girls are teary-eyed, and the boys are hiding their emotions in a game of shove and push.

The orchestra strikes the first chords of "Pomp and Circumstance," the sound drifting into the classrooms. We all line up as we rehearsed, dry our tears, straighten the ties the boys have managed to make crooked, and move smoothly into the stadium. Hoots and cheers and thunderous applause greet us. It's a heady moment. As I walk down the long aisle, I feel a warm tingle in my right hand and a bump on my upper arm. I realize my mother is standing by my side. She gestures toward where Gran is sitting and there stands my father behind Gran's seat with a bouquet of pink and lavender roses filling his arms. I'm breathless.

I have learned through my journey at The Nook that we are never alone. I get it now. Our ability to "see" beyond the veils that separate the worlds, the dimensions, is entirely up to us. I'm overjoyed that I have come to a place in my life where I'm able to glimpse the "other side," as it's called. I know deep in my heart that my parents are here to see me graduate; now my earlier sadness is gone, evaporated in a moment of clarity!

As I walk across the stage to receive my diploma, shaking the hands of our teachers and principal, I glance toward Gran and see her smiling as beautifully as I've ever seen her look. She too knows Mom and Dad are here with us. I guess they've been around for a lot of special occasions along the way, I just never knew.

As the evening draws to a close, the three muskateer-ettes gather in a quiet moment, share a group hug, promise that this isn't an end, but a beginning in our lives. Jazzy and Lexi have a surprise for me. They have applied to change their school location and transfer their scholarships as I have to the local campus of Penn State. Their plan is that we will all stay together. Even if this plan of theirs doesn't work out, my heart is so full of love it feels as though it will overflow. That's a good thing. To know I have such extraordinary friends that they would switch campuses and that their parents agreed gives me a very warm feeling.

Climbing into bed after the evening's festivities, I'm overwhelmed by a sense of security I haven't felt in a long while. Gran is positively glowing as she pops her head into my room to say good night. For the moment all is well in our world.

21

Meems Meets Emme

Can you believe it? I'm a working girl now! In the law office everyday nine to five, filing and answering the main bank of telephones. I'm also doing research in the legal library and guiding clients to the right attorney per their appointment. It's so much more than just the filing I had been doing and much more enjoyable. I'd never noticed how old the building is where the offices are located. There's a plaque by the door from the Historical Society saying the place was built in 1871. Lodged on a street filled with old homes, the three-story brick Victorian house we occupy is filled with large, rectangular windows, each surrounded by brick with concrete carvings. Even the third-story dormers are bordered by beautifully carved wood frames. Everything on the inside is hand-carved wood from the railings of the circular staircase to the baseboards and the crown moldings that draw the eyes to the vaulted ceilings. Natural light streams in everywhere. There's a lemony, woodsy smell to everything.

I've been given a little office in the back corner of the second floor. I love it. It's all mine! These days I light a jasmine candle on my desk and keep a small container of salt on the top of the filing cabinet. Each afternoon when the afternoon sun streams in through the window, sparkles dance around the room. And my little office has a ghost!

So, why do I think there's a ghost? I hear her. I feel an energy floating around, a female energy. Every now and then I feel her brush against my shoulder as I sit and work. When I use the filing room connected to my lovely little den, I always feel like I'm not alone. Thank goodness for the classes I've taken at The Nook, otherwise I might be too frightened to get any work done. I often find myself covered in goosebumps when I enter the room. One day when it's very quiet in the office, when no one else is about, I've decided I will work on communicating with my ghost.

*   *   *

Right before July fourth everyone goes away and I have the office all to myself. The day has arrived. It is July third and I am on my own for the holiday weekend. I start by lighting some traditional white sage, clearing the space of any negative energy that may be about, and follow that with my favorite frangipani incense lit with the flame of my special jasmine candle. Finishing with sweetness seals the cleared area and keeps any unwanted negative energy away. I spread my favorite blanket on the floor in front of my antique desk and sit quietly. Three deep, gentle, slow breaths later I'm transported beyond the veils and the room takes on a misty quality. Coming slowly into shape is the image of a young woman. Dressed in an outfit that is a mixture of silk, linen, and lace, with a high collar, tight waist, and a little flair in the skirt, this vision in off-white and lavender simply floats toward me. I'm amazed at the number of tiny buttons up the front of the dress and all along the sleeves. There's a soft rustle of material as she comes closer. She's even got a bustle with lots of material gathered and swept from the folded layers of the skirt! I wonder if she's wearing a corset underneath, her waist is so tiny!

Okay, I tell myself. *Get a grip, Meems, she's a ghost.*

I'm almost afraid to breathe or blink my eyes. Then I hear her. *I hear her!* She's speaking to me in the softest, most whispery voice.

"How do you do? My name is Emme. This was our home," she says. "I'm most delighted that those to whom

101

the house has been passed have honored its beauty and taken good and gentle care of it. I so loved living here as a girl I never wanted to leave. I had no idea that my desire to remain would so affect the path of our family. So strong was this desire, that the universe insured my not needing to leave by removing my parents." Whoa. At this point she starts to weep and pulls a beautiful lace handkerchief from inside her sleeve. Dabbing ever so gently at her eyes, she continues. "They had traveled to visit family in Ohio and on the way back, their carriage was struck by a runaway farm wagon and they were both crushed.

"When their will was read days after their funeral, I found out their entire estate was left to me. My grand-mother became my guardian. I was devastated. Now I did not wish to have the house at all. I wanted to run away. My grandmother, being the wise lady she was, allowed for my tantrums and tears. Months went by, as did my sixteenth birthday, and still I sat in my room, stared at nothing out my window and cried at my selfishness. This place where you are now was my room. Finally, when Grandmother felt enough time had passed, she initiated a 'program' she designed to get me back into the world again. She'd bustle into my room and throw open the curtains and the window, even in the winter. Said the fresh air was much needed and would do me good. The next step began when we started taking our meals in the garden. Again, she said the fresh air would do me good. The friends I had ignored in my utter grief for so long were still willing to come by and so we began to take tea together and talk about the news of the day. Grandmother had written a note to each of the families of my friends requesting they 'pop in.' Gradually, ever so slowly, it became easier to breathe when I awoke in the morning and I started to look forward to the days. A year had passed and I knew I had to get back to the fullness of life. I carried within me the slightest thread of sadness, which I hid from all I encountered.

"Grandmother's steps had become much slower and her energy was quite diminished. She knew her days were numbered and I refused to see it. A new bank had opened in the time of my yearlong hibernation and a very smart, kind young man was the branch manager. Grandmother introduced us one cold, windy March day. In a gust of wind my hat was pulled from my head, my hairpins all tumbling to the ground. Of course, that happened the moment we were about to enter the bank. A dapper young man flew out the door and ran down the street until the gust of wind that had snatched my hat from my very person died away and he was able to retrieve it. Grandmother was supremely impressed!

"As he handed me back my totally destroyed hat, our eyes met, and I instantly knew he was all my tomorrows. We married three months later; and, in the house I never wanted to leave, we raised our four children and grew old together. My grandmother left us to join my parents before our first wedding anniversary had arrived. She loved my Garrett as much as I did, adored our first child, yet needed to be with her daughter, my mother. And so we said goodbye. Her bed was right there over by the window. She had moved into my room when Garrett and I married. One starry night, as I was tucking her in, our roles now reversed, she took my hand and in the tiniest voice said it was time for her to go. Then she looked up into the sky and closed her eyes. I carry that thread of sadness too.

"I am happy you are here in this office, Meems. I like you; I like the caregivers of the property. If you don't mind, I will stay."

Finally, she came up for air, took a breath so to speak, and I think I took my first breath since she'd started her tale. I couldn't believe how her story was so akin to mine. I too carry a deep sadness that the outside world doesn't get to see. My grandmother is the most important person in my life. Even our names were similar, same letters! I felt as though I'd made a new friend. Finally, I nodded. I was so dumbstruck I couldn't think of anything to say.

Emme smiled at me and said, "We will talk again another time. For now, know that I am with you here, you are never alone. Never alone, Meems." And with that, the mist cleared and she was gone.

I can't wait to tell Gran about this "visit" and then I'll get Lexi and Jazzy on FaceTime. Did I mention they ended up going to University Park for the summer session? Their excuses for changing their program and location didn't fly with those in charge at the university. I miss them, but FaceTime has been a blessing! They'll love what I have to tell them! I sure do. I'm so glad Gran dragged me to the Seekers Body, Mind, and Spirit Expo, not to mention how grateful I am to the ladies of The Nook and all their lit classes!

22

You Never Know

You know how you never know what twists and turns your life will take? No one knows when their parents are going to go. Most get to have a lifetime with them. Then, when they're old, the adult children bury their folks. Not me. I think that was the first twist. I was four years old when my parents died, taken from me by someone who had too much to drink. I would be lying if I said I didn't miss them every day. There have been so many milestones they've not been here for. I think they call it twists and turns because that's how your stomach feels when huge things come along and knock the wind out of you. You feel all twisted and warped deep in your gut. It's like you can't stand up straight anymore. You can't eat because it feels like if you swallow there's nowhere for the food to go; you're all blocked off. Those are the dark twists and turns. Even in the dark moments you can be surprised by unexpected bits of light sparkling around you. Ever since the Seekers Body, Mind, and Spirit Expo and meeting Artie and Bitsy, Lesley and Moraine, I feel like I have a lot of those sparkling twists and turns happening to me.

Having the teachers at The Nook on my side, all of them, has been such a boost. The dawning of understanding of the energies around me, the layers of life that exist and can be touched when you part the veils that most cannot see, have all been so uplifting. My relationship with Gran, always so precious, has become deeper and much more profound, our conversations expansive, encompassing, and all around far more honest and open. I'm often amazed at the levels we touch upon in the quietest moments of being together. My best pals have become more open to the colors and textures of their lives and their relationships and we are more bonded than ever before. Maybe, best of all, I don't feel near as alone as I used to

What's ahead doesn't scare me near as much as it used to. I've come to appreciate how much more there is to me than I'd ever thought. It's like I lived under a really heavy cloud for a long time and the sun has finally come back. You never know what's around the bend.

23

Change Doesn't Have to Hurt

Summer is speeding by, like somebody opened the center of the hourglass and the sand is slipping through faster and faster. Happily, once again, we are in an off cycle for chemo, so Gran is doing well. Work at the law office has been too hectic to have the time to sit in the garden, or anywhere else in the building to experience the ghosties I know hang out in the old house. One of these days I will have the place all to myself again, find a spot where I will light my candles and incense, and circle my stones and simply be. I will see if Emme has anything else to share with me and see if I can get her to bring in any other spirits that are in the house. I'd love to meet them.

In the meantime, I'm doing a really great job of keeping up with my meditations. It's amazing how it feels when you can clear all the chatter from your head. Relaxation flows through you just as your blood streams through your body. I've also gotten really good at knowing my guides are with me, working with me. I can especially feel my protector guide, Running Bull, every time I get in the car, take a walk, or need extra protection. My joy guide, Morning Star, brings me laughter in the most unexpected moments, sometimes when I absolutely should not be grinning or chuckling, and my doctor of philosophy, Hermes, has practically been throwing a collection of great books at my feet, so much so that I actually tripped over one the other day at Main Street Books. Main Street is a really special little bookstore where the spiritual reading section is superb. This summer I've devoured Michael Roads, Wayne Dyer, Byron Katie, Carolyn Myss, Louise Hay, Jane Roberts, and Ted Andrews, just to mention the big ones! I'm about to get into the channeled works of Paul Selig. Way back in the 1970s Jane Roberts wrote channeled work from an entity called Seth. Heavy-duty stuff! They say Paul Selig's work must be read and reread to get the threads of strength and change the books offer so you can weave them into your life. Of course, I'll be starting school soon, my first year of college, and I'm absolutely positive my "fun" reading time will be greatly reduced.

The last guide I will mention for now who I've been working closely with is my doctor of healing, Galen of

Pergamum. Galen is a quiet yet powerful energy that comes to me in white and gold. His voice is always gentle yet extremely insistent when he speaks to me. With his guidance I've made some small changes to Gran's and my diet. We've eliminated most of the processed sugar we used to eat and food in a box that only needs nuked is a bygone. I won't say I'm excited by all the veggies we eat, but still, we're both in better shape. I really enjoyed the assortment and abundance of fresh fruit we bought at the farmers' market this summer. I will miss it in the winter months. Apples in fall are good, not so much in the cold weather months. We've totally stopped eating red meat and only have white meat a few times a month. I've even learned to enjoy the textures and flavors of different fresh fish that the farmers' market offers.

As I reflect on the changes that have happened since spring, I'm not sure I'd say I'm overwhelmed, just a little more than super thrilled at the turn life has taken for both me and my gran! Once upon a time I was terrified of any kind of change. Change took my parents away and all the potential events and people that might have been. Now I understand that we create the change we want to happen and we are the commanders of our days. How you think will become what you experience. I so get that. I don't always keep my thoughts high and cheery, I'm not yet that balanced. I sure am enjoying the journey to get there though! Sometimes I feel like I'm climbing a mountain, sometimes I feel like I've reached a really, nicely elevated place on the mountain, and sometimes I feel like I've slid almost to the foot of the mountain. Those are the days when I know I have a lot of growing to do!

24

Distractions

So here I stand, my first day of college at Penn State, Ogontz Campus, Abington, PA. Looking up at the massive, old, stone buildings takes my breath away. Isn't it interesting how I go from one old building to another? Ghosties at college, who'd have thought? I'm ready to start! My class list, location of classes, and book list came by email about three weeks ago, so Gran and I drove over to the campus bookstore and bought the books I need for this semester. Then we took a slow stroll around the campus to make note of where the buildings I need to know to get to classes are located. Somehow the buildings didn't look as intimidating when Gran was at my side. I need to suck it up and drop the fear. What could possibly happen that I couldn't handle?

Since I have no idea what I want to do when I'm finished with school, I'm taking the basics this year: English, math, history, and a touch of science. I wish I were at Hogwarts School of Witchcraft and Wizardry and I could take Divination, Astronomy and Charms. Of course, I can take those courses at The Nook, and I will as they come up. I'll have to really organize my time so I can keep up with my college studies, be able to take classes at The Nook, and work part-time at the law office. My most important time will be spent with Gran and my best girls. Have you noticed how well I can dawdle? It is time to go into the building. I do love the mixture of modern and old architecture here and I'm happy my first class is in one of the new buildings. Imagine if I were to start class and a spirit were to sit and chat with me. Oh, the distraction that would be!

Speaking of distractions, why did the most gorgeous of gorgeous guys have to sit right next to me? Blue eyes, dark brown hair, tall and hot; I hope I'm not staring or drooling!

"Hi," he says as he extends his right hand. "I'm Avery. And you are?"

His voice is deep and silky, with a mild timbre. OMG! Now am I supposed to say Mary Elizabeth? Ugh! That's such an old-fashioned name. And, he's waiting for a response. You'd think I'd never talked to a guy before.

"Meems" pops out of my mouth.

Because I don't take his big extended hand, he withdraws it very casually. "Well, that's certainly unusual. Are you a local girl?" Whaaat! Does he think I have an accent or just that my name is weird? "Meems," he says. "Exotic, different, delightful!"

Now I can't think at all. Oh, why me, shy me, why today?

Just as I'm about to barf up another one-word reply, the instructor walks in the door and the silence in the room becomes deafening. Avery grins at me and says, "Later!"

I whip my head around to the front of the class to do my best to pay attention. This being English, I know it will be one of my easiest classes. Still, one has to focus. Oh yes, focus; time to take three deep, slow breaths. How could I have forgotten that so easily? Darn that Avery. A big, deep sigh escapes from me…did he hear that?

Ninety minutes later I think I've fallen in love with the teacher. He's probably fiftyish and he loves our language. Listening to him is like hearing the strokes of a paintbrush as it slides over a canvas. Colors explode in the words he shares. He shapes them like Michelangelo with clay in his hands. So what if he's asked us to cover over one hundred pages in our books tonight? Tonight, not tonight, I was going to go to the beginner psychic development class one more time before moving into the more advanced group. So, the tug on my time starts with the first day of college. Ugh!

25

Funny How Things Are

After a long and pretty exciting day, I'm ready to go home and tell Gran every detail about every course and instructor. I've also met some nice people just starting out like me. And then there is Avery. We share three classes and he sat near me in each and every class. I could feel his energy. It was drifting off of him like he was some sort of electric heater. Warm, soft, enveloping vibrations emanating with each full breath he took. Why do I know that? Why am I thinking such things? Oh geesh!

Wouldn't you know just as I get to my car all of my books drop out of my book bag. I was rushing to get out of the parking lot before running into Avery again. He makes my pulse race and my eyes fog! And who, of course, saves me? Avery! We're parked next to each other. I know they say the world is small, but this small? Then he says, "I know for some reason my energies are making you uncomfortable. That's the last thing I want to happen when I'm about to make a new friend. I hope you don't think I'm off my rocker and I will do my best to create some energetic distance, at least until you are more at ease around me. I do have a high vibration and when I saw your aura, I figured you did too. I may be more used to the energy than you are in crowds. We both have the gift of the empath in us."

I know my eyes are rounder than they've ever been, and I hope my jaw hasn't dropped low enough for him to see my teeth! I'm astounded. My first day of college and the first guy I meet is into energy stuff!

I drag my tongue back into my mouth and as casually as possible say, "I'm cool. I was feeling the energy coming from you and I wasn't sure what to do about it." Like I was going to tell him he scared the bejeesus out of me. I continue, "I have to get home to my gran right now. Maybe one day we can grab a coffee together and talk about empathic energy." Oh gawd, did I just ask him out? What's the matter with me?

He gives me a brilliant smile, nods his head, and says, "That, Meems, is a date! I'll see you in class tomorrow. I looked over your shoulder when you had your roster out and we have a lot of the same courses scheduled. Have a great night. Bye!"

Have a great night? Have a *great night*? I can't even catch my breath. What in this world is going on here? I throw my book bag into the back seat and jump into the front as fast as I can. He waits for me to pull out first. Gran would say he is a first-class gentleman, offering his hand for a gentlemanly shake of introduction. Oh, I just remembered that's the first step in psychometry. He was going to read my energies! And he picked up my books much in the same way Garrett chased after Emme's hat! This is so Victorian! He's just a guy, right? He's just a really cute, really nice, maybe even spiritual guy...my age! Wait until Jazzy and Lexi hear about this. I hope their first days at school were just as rad! I'm guessing not or they would have told me.

I miss my girls. They came home for a quick visit at the end of the summer session and left about a week ago to settle into their dorms. They are in the rooms we were all going to live in together at Main. I have lots of pictures though and it looks all good. If I had gone to Happy Valley too, I would never have met Avery. Funny how the universe works, isn't it?

26

Avery and The Nook

Doing a lot of studying at the library with Avery gives us plenty of time to simply chat. In these little chats I have discovered a very spiritual, metaphysical side to Avery, so I've decided to introduce him to The Nook. The other day I gave him their calendar and he went right to their website. He carried on for several minutes about how he couldn't believe he'd never heard of The Nook and how it was right in his own backyard! Then he realized he was going on quite a bit, turned bright red, and buried his head in his books. I thought it was kind of cute. We've decided to go to the beginner psychic development class Monday evening as his introduction to the school.

*　　*　　*

Well, this is exciting! It's Monday and Avery and I have just arrived at The Nook and there's a large group in attendance. I like when there are only three or four people for class; it makes it very intimate. On the other hand, when there's a larger group the messages really flow. Tonight will be a night of flow. Lesley begins the class with a prayer of protection and a lovely meditation to relax everyone and help us all gather our thoughts. Out of the corner of my eye I see Avery nodding his head in agreement to the lesson Lesley is leading. I'm glad. I was so nervous to have him enter this very private aspect of myself. This is my world, or at least that's the way I think of being at The Nook. I notice he is also being very quiet.

It's his turn to give a message. Lesley invites Avery to the front of the room, gets him to settle in, focus, and find his joy guide. Avery closes his eyes and begins to describe a scruffy little boy with bare feet and blond hair. The little one introduces himself as Addison. He tells Avery he likes *A* names. Avery's eyes pop open in surprise and delight. He shoots me a very sheepish grin.

Lesley asks if he's ready to give someone a message. He nods his head and closes his eyes again. Avery takes a deep breath, then opening his eyes, and holding his dominant hand straight out in front of him, he begins to walk around the room, stopping at each person to get a sense of their energy. Lesley reminds Avery to take his time and that Addison will indicate who the message is for if Avery pays attention to the energy in his extended hand.

Avery walks toward a lady who is fairly new in the class and says, "This lady. Addison is yelling in my head and my hand is superhot all of sudden."

She looks up and quietly says, "My name is Karli."

Avery then asks, "Karli, would you like a message from my joy guide, Addison? And, oh, my name is Avery!" This last part he blurts out.

Karli nods to Avery and Lesley reminds us all we need to hear each other's voices loud and clear to help establish a heart-bridge connection. So, Karli looks up to Avery and says in a very clear voice, "I would love a message from your joy guide, Addison, Avery."

Avery closes his eyes once again and begins the message. "Addison is telling me to tell you that the move was the right thing to do. You need to trust yourself; you know what is right for you. You have forgotten to trust yourself because of what you think were mistakes in relationships that left you hurt."

His eyes pop open and he looks at Karli, who is sitting in the corner of the couch, crying quietly. "Oh my God," she says. "How would you know I've just moved here from Colorado? I left to be able to start over again after being hurt very badly by people I thought were my friends as well as my coworkers. I was so wrong about them and because of that lost a very important promotion. I have been wondering if I'd done the right thing, or if I'd simply run away. I have to start all over again. Thank you for that message. I needed to hear that I must get back to trusting myself. Now all I need to do is find a new job!" With that she smiled at Avery, who seemed rooted to the spot where he stood in front of her.

Lesley prompted him to "close the bridge" with gratitude and sit down. I know just how Avery felt. I felt the same sense of shock and wonder that he was feeling right then when I'd given my first message and it was right on target. I mean bull's-eye!

The evening came to a close after a few more messages. Lesley reminded us we are simply the voice box for our guides and must give what we get whether we understand it or not. She also repeated the "no negatives" rule.

Avery and I stopped at the Koffee Korner hut just down the street on the way to our cars and sat over hot cocoa to talk about the class. "Thanks for inviting me here, Meems. I learned tonight that many of the thoughts that seem to slip into my head out of nowhere about people around me have been insights from my guides. I'm going to study the take-home folder of information on this class and the guides. I can't wait to come back, meet all five of my guides, and work them. It's time to really get into my intuition and use it more often."

And then he took my hand, which was lying on the table next to my hot mug of dark chocolate sweetness. Whoa, I'm not ready for relationship stuff beyond friendship, so I slowly and gently slide my hand back to my cup hoping he doesn't notice. Duh, Meems, of course he noticed. He cleared his throat and pushed his chair back. I chugged the last sip of cocoa and stood up. We walked quietly to our cars and said good night. What a night!

27

Halloween and Spirits

Pop quizzes and exams, lots of late-night study sessions in my warm, cozy bedroom, and I seem to be zipping through the semester. I chat with Jazzy and Lexi every weekend, work Saturdays at the law office, and chill with Gran on Sundays. And here we are, all of a sudden nearing Halloween and then Thanksgiving. The girls will be home for the fall-winter break, and I can't wait. I suppose you're wondering about Avery. We're good friends and go to classes at The Nook weekly. We've progressed to the intermediate class in development and the messages are really powerful. The exciting news is that there will be what is called an "old-fashioned sit" at The Nook. What, you may wonder, is a "sit"? Well, I'll tell you. It's bringing in whatever spirits are about and getting messages from them to share. I can't wait and Gran is going to come with me.

As the weather has become definitely fall cool, she seems to be more tired than ever and has come to prefer having her friends visit her rather than going out and about. Thankfully, she is off of chemo for a while now and her cough is barely there. The doctors aren't using the word *remission*, though they are saying they are satisfied with Gran's status right now. Have I mentioned I can't stand doctors? They seem to *not* have been schooled in the art of knowing the origins of a disease. That really bugs me! We are keeping up with the Reiki appointments and I believe *they* are the main reason Gran is holding her own.

Here we are, October 31, Halloween, when the veils (a kind of energetic curtain) between the worlds are the very thinnest! Avery, Gran, and I have arrived at The Nook. There is a crowd! The place is lit in candlelight and is glowing, and the shadows all seem to be dancing. You can actually feel the many spirits that have come to the open portal of The Nook. Artie and Bitsy always do a super thorough spiritual cleansing of the place before this annual event. Of course, they keep The Nook spiritually cleansed every day, so we are all safe and free to be ourselves. All the chairs are in an oval, with the large pieces of furniture pushed out of the way. You can feel the excitement and energy in the air. The evening begins with an explanation of how a "sit" works and how important it is to participate. If one of the mediums describes someone even remotely familiar, we need to speak up and claim the energy. Then Artie recited the circle of protection prayer and we began.

The first "people" to arrive were my parents with a message for everyone: "When you are well and whole within yourself, you are in nourishment of others. You feed a need, a need where all ought to experience love. Be well. Be loved. Know you are never alone."

Okay, wow, not what I was thinking they would say. I was hoping for a "we love *you*, Meems" kind of message. Though it would be just like my folks to take care of the many!

The next three visitors were relatives of people attending the sit, and then a group of "ancients" arrived. You could feel the room get really thick with energy. Artie welcomed them and asked if they had a message to share. They went to Avery and stood before him. You could see he could feel the energy in front of him from the way he tilted his head back; he couldn't "see" them though. Artie asked Avery if he'd like a message. He remembered the rule about answering the query in a very clear, affirmative way to make the strongest connection, so he said, "Oh yes!"

She closed her eyes for a moment, lowered her head a bit, took a deep, cleansing breath and began to speak. "You are not your family, young man. We see you in the light that you are. When you are being honest with yourself, it becomes clear that the history you believe to be yours is simply a story vibrating around you in a low frequency. You have the power not to invest in the story, to see it as it really is, an agreement those around you made to experience what they need to learn and grow. Step back and allow for those around you to find their own way. In doing that, your way becomes 'clear.'"

Avery, with eyes absolutely as wide open as they could be, thanked the ancients and Artie for the message and said he would take it with him and think deeply about it.

The evening went on and many more spirits came to visit. Some were pets who'd passed over; there were old friends who came in, teachers, and of course lots of relatives. What a stupendous night. The last person to receive a message was my gran. Her healing guide came in, told her not to worry about her health, that she wasn't finished yet on the earth plane and that she had more support to keep her going than she realized. Airmed, a Celtic goddess connected with healing, turned out to be Gran's healing guide. She told her to stay with the current program and all would be well for a while. Gran nodded her understanding of the message and thanked Airmed and then the evening was over.

I wanted to ask Airmed a few questions of my own concerning Gran, even though I knew the message was hers and hers alone. Still, I had the questions. I decided to wait a few days and then approach Gran. Avery was very quiet and said he had a lot to think about. He never really spoke about his family and I realized he always changed the subject whenever it came up. His life at home must have been a challenge. I guess we all have challenges.

28

In Gratitude, Sugar Cookies, and Pumpkin Pie

When you're a kid, Halloween is simply a great time to dress up as silly as you can and collect a ton of candy. Knowing the veils between the worlds was so thin at the end of October made it seem like an altogether different holiday. The energy everywhere had a special, significant, and supercharged feeling. Now that we're on our way to Thanksgiving, I can definitely feel the change in the air. Fall is fully upon us and the leaves are floating gently to the ground, painted in gemstone colors, taking with them every story of every tree.

We studied a book at The Nook written by a monk named Adyashanti. He explained that the leaves on a tree hold the stories of that particular tree. Every tree has its own stories. When the leaves turn color they are dying, returning to feed the earth. He said the trees know this is the way of things, and you'd never see a tree bend over and scoop up the fallen leaves feeling the need to hold on to their stories. Only human beings do that. They hold every story they've ever experienced. I don't want to do that. I don't want to carry the weight of a lifetime of leaves. Have you ever raked a yard full of leaves and then tried to drag the trash bag out of the yard? It weighs a ton. I like the analogy! Like I said, I'm not going to do that!

Gran wants me to invite Avery over for Thanksgiving dinner. Gran feels he needs the energy around him of people who love and care for each other. Well, Gran and I certainly fit that bill. I have to figure out how to ask him without giving him the impression I feel sorry for him. He's been rather quiet since the "sit" at The Nook. Don't get me wrong, we still spend hours together at the library. He's just so serious. It's almost as if he closed something down. I hope not. I enjoy his friendship. We're kind of like a couple, except we don't go a lot of places socially. I work, he works, we study, and we each have responsibilities at home. On the other hand, we aren't seeing other people. I've been asked out a few times; the guys seemed nice, but they asked me during the times when Gran was in her chemo routine and I needed to be there for her so I declined. I really like that Avery and I have developed a wonderful friendship; I hope that a deep trust will develop for us both where the other is concerned. From the few things he's shared it seems as though he is the main caregiver in his family.

The other day he arrived late for our early morning study period smelling like a bakery. When I pointed out he smelled like sugar cookies, he blushed and said he was baking cupcakes with his little sister so she'd have something to take to school for the fund-raiser her class was doing. He didn't want her to be the only one without something to give, and he said it was time for her to learn how to bake anyway. I asked him how he'd learned to bake and he said when he was very young his mother used to bring him into the kitchen when she cooked and if he was good, he got to help. He said after everything went wrong, those were the times he held on to. I didn't ask him what "went wrong" meant. It didn't feel like the right time. I did ask him if he was cooking for Thanksgiving for his family and he said there was no Thanksgiving dinner at his house. His siblings were being sent to their father's and his mother wouldn't be coming out of her room or her bottle. So, I said, "Hey, why don't you join me and Gran and we'll have a cook-off contest. Gran says she makes the best stuffing in the world. I know my cranberry relish is to die for and you can show off your skills with dessert!"

Avery looked me in the eye, like seriously, eye to eye, then he smiled and said, "You're on! I love a good challenge!"

Well, that went better than I thought it would and I opened to a life lesson. Why attach an outcome to something that hasn't happened yet? Why decide how things will be for another person? Lao Tzu was an ancient philosopher and it is told that he said, "If you are depressed you are living in the past. If you are anxious you are living in the future. If you are at peace you are living in the present." I'd like to live in peace and not think I know better than someone else what's good for them, nor do I want to worry about what hasn't happened yet! You know, learning the lesson of living life at a higher vibration is a very satisfying feeling.

*   *   *

Thanksgiving Day has been wonderful; Gran simply sparkled and glowed with as close to good health as I've seen her in a long time. Turns out Avery whipped up the most delicious sugar cookies I've ever eaten and his pumpkin pie was to die for. Jazzy and Lexi arrived just in time for dessert and Avery adopted two new best friends. I'm glad everyone got along so well. I hadn't realized how important it was to me that we all get along. The blending of personalities was as smooth as Avery's pumpkin-pie filling! We made plans to get together tomorrow to have a day of play. Gran suggested we spend the day doing something outdoors. It won't do her any harm to sit still and rest after standing on her feet all day and entertaining as she hasn't in a very long time. Though I'm sure the food and the laughter were better for her than any medicine could ever be. And laugh we did. Let's see, there was the side-hugging laughter when Avery plugged in the blender to puree the pumpkin but forgot to lock the lid down. It was like an orange rocket was launched right into his shocked face. Then there was the moment Gran took her old cane-bottom folding chairs out of the closet, sat down to rest her weary bones a moment, and literally had her bottom stuck in the seat of the chair as the old cane disintegrated. And, to make it worse, she was laughing so hard she couldn't pry herself loose. Poor Avery, poor Gran! You might be wondering if I was able to pull off a catastrophe-free day. I'll be honest, I did really well, right up until I locked myself out of the house walking my girls to their car. By the time I rang the doorbell, Gran and Avery were in the front hall having a real guffaw together. Being my stubborn self, I waited until I was chilled to the bone to ring the doorbell and they knew it. They knew it!

29

Something to Be Truly Grateful For

At the end of the day, as I settled in, totally relaxed and bone-tired under my silky lavender, blue, and mint green comforter, I had a sense I wasn't alone. At that moment there appeared in the corner of my room a column of baby blue light with sparkles, like twinkling stars hovering just above my floor. The glitter coalesced and quite slowly two figures stepped out of the column as though they'd just come out of a turnstile door. My mom and dad simply stepped into my bedroom.

"Look who I brought with me this time, Meems," said my mother in her clearest voice. My dad just stood there grinning. All this time had passed, and he stands there grinning and not saying a word. That temper I'm famous for was starting to get hot!

"Dad, aren't you going to say something? Anything?

Geesh!" I said in a not-too-calm or quiet voice. And still he stood there with a lopsided smile on his face.

"Meems, honey," Mom interjected, "this is his first time leaving the astral and I think he's a bit mystified."

"Dad, come and sit on my bed."

"Why, Meems, that would be splendid. I'm blown away at how you've grown. It feels like we've only been gone a moment."

Mom's eyes open so wide at that statement that it looks as though her eyebrows have disappeared under her bangs. She's wearing a very familiar "oh dear" face.

"Yes," I say, "he did just say that. Well, let me set the record straight, Dad, you've been gone—" I never got to finish that sentence as at that very moment Gran burst through the door.

"Ohhh!" she exclaimed. "I just knew my baby was here. I could feel the energies of the house shift. What a wonderful day for a visit. The moon is full, the day filled with joy and life, and here you are. What a blessing this is to this old woman."

"Mom, stop that. You aren't old at all. Yes, I know you struggle with your health these days. Your time has not come. You've much to do here and our Meems needs you. Come and sit with us."

And everybody climbed onto my bed—me, Gran, Mom, and Dad. Weird thing is I felt both of my parents when they sat down. I felt the bed shift. This is so over the top and I love it. Thank goodness I've been to so many classes at The Nook or I would have missed this very precious gathering. We chatted the night away. I caught Mom and Dad up on all the stories I thought were important for them to know, though as the night wore on, they finished the stories with me. That's when I knew for sure they'd always been with me. Gran and Mom spoke quietly, weaving their conversation through the night with the threads of my stories. Neither was loud enough for me to hear. I hope Gran will share their conversation with me when this time together is over.

Mom and Dad shared the details of their healing journey with me. They explained what a shock it was to their bodies, minds, and spirits as the other car crashed into them and they knew they would not survive. Dad described the being that came and collected them and took their auric bodies to the Center for Healing where beings of light worked to heal the damage of the accident to their energetic bodies. Once Dad started talking it was hard for Mom to get even one word out. He hadn't used his "vocals," as he called them, in so long, it took him a while to get going. It also took a good deal of energy to produce a body for me to see.

When the night turned to morning and the sparkling blue column returned to the corner of my room, though

Gran and I weren't ready to part with them, they stood as one and walked together to the column and in a flash were gone. They said as they left that they were always close by and all we needed to do was "give a yell" when we needed them, and they'd be there for us. Gran and I sat with our arms around each other, on my bed under my silky blanket, excited, content, and dumbfounded. What a wild night. What an extraordinary Thanksgiving. Gran went to the kitchen, brought us each a piece of Avery's pumpkin pie loaded with whipped cream and a cup of cocoa also loaded with whipped cream. With our bellies full, we drifted off to sleep together. Something we hadn't done since I was a little girl.

30

Wishes Do Come True

Finals are this week, with new classes coming in January. I wonder what the New Year will bring. More than that do I know what I want? First, I want Gran's diagnosis to be reversed. Cancer gone! Next, I want to keep my 4.0 average at school. Third, I wouldn't mind winning the lottery, ha-ha! Mostly I want Gran to be healthy. A boyfriend would be nice. Avery and I are close, and I enjoy that he gets me and my spiritual life. Sadly, with his family life so complicated, and him being such an honorable guy, he has no room emotionally for a girl-friend. I'm eternally grateful to have found his friendship and will always cherish him. Whomever I date, however deep the feelings get, they will need to understand how important my friendships are to me and that I will always make time for my friends.

I took my last exam this afternoon, thank goodness. Feels like I aced each test this week. That's a load off my shoulders. Next big thing on the schedule is Gran's oncologist appointment. I hope I'm not dreaming, but since Thanksgiving she has had a bounce in her step, her coloring is pinker than it has been in a long time, and she barely coughs!

On a lark, I went to a candle magic class at The Nook. Avery and I had an open Thursday afternoon after finals week, so we popped in. I was blown away by the power a candle carries and delivers. I never thought about cleaning my candles before this class and will never light a candle again without cleaning it. Who knew the energies of every person involved in the making, packing, stacking, and selling of candles ended up in the candle itself?

I always felt colors were important, and the more classes I take at The Nook the more I realize what an impact the colors around us have on our energies, thoughts, and feelings. Anyway, I've been lighting blue candles with little circles called "petitions" under them every day since the class. Once I get my candles clean, I write my intention for the burning of the candle and place the little circle under it. I've been extremely focused and clear as I expressed the intention of Gran being healthy once again. I think if she believes she is well, and I know she is better, we will have a positive outcome at the doctor.

Have I mentioned that I can't stand doctors' offices? I'm not crazy about doctors either. I much prefer holistic, fundamental practitioners, especially the ones that work with energies. Anyway, here we are at the big check-up. I did the circle of protection prayer around me and Gran before we entered the building, as I anticipated the others there for appointments would not be of the highest vibrations. There is so much suffering in illness and much illness in suffering. I can feel Gran's trepidation like a tight spandex girdle around her body and I want to support her in the best way I can, so I take her hand into mine. She had them folded in her lap, on top of her purse with her fingers interlaced, and she was squeezing them so hard, the color had all but drained away. She turns her head to look at me. I lift an eyebrow and see the dawning of recognition in her eyes that she was letting fear push aside all her positive thoughts and feelings. She closed her eyes and took a long, deep breath to center herself back in the light of positivity. I instantly felt her body relax. And I must say I'm tickled over how deep a breath she took. That seems to me to bode well for this visit.

We are called to the inner sanctum of the offices and led to a lovely office decorated in beautiful mahogany furniture and colors of rose and gold. There's a good energy filling the room. I'm pleasantly surprised. The doctor comes in, greets Gran warmly, and introduces himself to me. Oncologists tend to work in teams these days; there are so many people going through a journey of cancer that many are needed to guide, create, and institute all the protocols in what they call the "war on cancer." Gran and I decided early on we weren't going to war, yet you can't change the common language of the journey. We simply created our own language.

He sits down behind his huge desk, folds his hands together over a very thick file, looks down, takes a deep breath, raises his head to look into Gran's eyes, and I'm about to faint. Then he smiles the most radiant smile I've ever seen and speaks. "I am thrilled to tell you the protocols worked. The pictures we took of your lungs this past week are clear. Your blood work is strong and clear as well. Your white blood cell count is in just the right range. You need to take your time and rebuild your immune system. I'd like for you to add elderberry syrup to your vitamin regimen and join a gym. We'll bring you back in three months and look things over just as thoroughly then. In the meantime, you are in remission. Keep up the good work! Any questions, ladies?"

I'm not even able to think right now, and he asks if we have any questions. I look at Gran and her face is shining. We both have the kind of tears that glisten and don't spill out of your eyes and both of our mouths are hanging open! Then Gran nods her head to the doctor, stands up.

and says, "I'm happy to hear you say what I knew when I walked in here today. Thank you for all you've done this past year. I'll see you in few months. Let's hit the road, Meems." She shakes hands with the grinning man; I thank him and shake his hand too.

Together we made a beeline to the door. It felt like the elevator ride took forever. When the doors opened, we hotfooted it into the parking lot where we both started jumping up and down, hooting, whooping, and laughing all at the same time.

We called Lexi, Jazzy, and Avery and invited them over for a celebratory dinner. Christmas this year was going to be extraordinary! Yup, wishes do come true.

31

Night Brings a Big Moment

This was a day filled with body shots of adrenaline! With the excitement of the news that Gran was in great shape, being tickled that the oncologist told her to use elderberry syrup, which would rebuild her immune system, and then having a celebratory dinner, by the time I got to bed, I was beyond tired and revved up at the same time. I climbed into bed hoping to fall right to sleep. Not! My room lit up with a kaleidoscope of colors; a blast of hot lava crossed my bed and the room disappeared into a mist. The energies were so strong my head felt as though it was expanding beyond my skull.

Okay, this is a little scary. A gentle voice said, "Really, young lady, fear from you to me. Let me help you release that fear, I'm your master guide. It's time for us to begin to work together. You're ready."

I'm ready? Ready to work with my master guide? Whoa! Okay, I hadn't realized I'd come this far. At least she didn't call me little one. Well, bring it on, I say!

I remember at my first development class at The Nook I learned it was important to speak out loud when meeting your guides to establish a strong connection. Now I blurt out, "Oh cool. Hi, I'm Meems." Duh, like she doesn't know me. "May I have your name, please?" Now I'm stuck. I don't know what else to say. I hope she answers me.

"My name is White Sage. I've watched you working diligently with your inner band guides and I'm proud of the way you've blossomed. In order to continue on this path there is one event in your life that you need to revisit and release. Do you know what it is I'm bringing to you, young lady?"

Well, darned if I know. Oh, I probably shouldn't have thought that. White Sage can hear everything.

"Close your eyes, Meems, we're going to take a journey together. Begin with your three deep breaths."

I settle in and breathe; suddenly we are on the beach. We seem to be hovering, or apart from the scene in front of us. I see me as a toddler, playing in the sand with my dad. Morning Star (my joy guide) appears and Running Bull (my protector guide) steps in. And now I'm surrounded by all five of my guides. Hermes (my Doctor of Philosophy) as well as Galen (my healing guide) have joined us and created a circle around me. I'm trying not to be frightened, but I've never had all of my guides arrive at the same time. What could possibly be so bad that they all need to be with me? What do I need that much protection from?

I love watching my younger self building sandcastles with my dad. We were so happy playing in the sunshine. Oh my, oh my, oh my, now I remember. It's going to get very dark. A huge cloud is going to block the light and a voice is going to announce, "We are the darkness, we are here to harvest. We will take those we wish to have."

I know a hand is going to come and pluck people off the beach, including my mom and dad. I remember the nightmare, the all-encompassing fear. At least I'd thought it was a nightmare. My parents died in the accident a short time later. I'd had a metaphoric vision of something yet to happen. Then I blocked it from my mind, removed it from my heart, and decided it never happened. Even though I was so young, I knew this dark image was a part of my parents having been taken away from me.

I understand why all of my guides are here. "White Sage, why are you making me do this? Why now? Why couldn't it stay buried?" My questions are tinged with anger and shoot from me like the bullets from an automatic weapon. I hate guns. I hate this!

She answers immediately. "Young lady, this you must

release to be able to become all you are meant to be. You are destined to be a 'traveler.' You will move through what the third dimension calls time, and you will bring healing to the multitudes.

"You won't be able to reach this place of evolution until you heal the gaping wound this vision has caused. Your parents had a sacred contract to fulfill. Your foresight was not the reason for their deaths. Let go, Meems. Allow that dark place in your heart to fill with light. You're now reconnected to your parents; you know they're in your life and always will be. Let go of the gloom the vision brought. Breathe deep, release; fill the space with love and light; take your power back."

I know White Sage is right. I relax, bring in healing light, see my parents glowing above us and instantly feel the last vestige of the darkness in my heart being released. What a feeling of freedom. One by one my guides leave until it's only me and White Sage. "Good work, young lady, good work. Now your path is clear. We will meet again soon."

With that I was back in my bed. It felt as though it was spinning under me, but I was at least in my room, feeling safe and sound and just a little freaked out. Well, hasn't this been quite the day! I will keep my introduction to White Sage to myself for now.

32

Listen, Simply Listen

Morning came sooner than I expected. I was different. I wondered if anyone would notice. Most important though was to celebrate Gran's recovery!

It took a few days for the glow to slow after we found out she was free. Gran asked if I had any special plans Saturday after work; she said it was time for us to have a chat. Somehow, I knew this was going to be a deep chat, good but deep. Not at all like when I was young and she called me on the carpet for a chat. "Mary Elizabeth Emily Mearcham," she would say. "We need to talk." When she said my name that way, I knew I was in trouble and we were about to have a heavy conversation!

I finished my work early Saturday and entered the house, which smelled delightful from the chocolate brownies baking in the oven. Good omen for a talk! Gran was in the kitchen with a cup of her favorite peppermint tea steaming in front of her and a plate of fresh brownies on the table. I poured myself a glass of chocolate milk and sat down across from her.

Gran spoke. "Let's get right to it, my darling girl."

I nodded, thinking this must be really big. She didn't even say hello.

She continued, "We've had a tough year to be sure. I'm very proud of the way you handled yourself. I'm also very happy at the way you opened your spirit to learning and accepting new and exciting lessons. The entire year was about learning lessons. I certainly had my own!" I wondered if Gran was going to pause to take a breath. She did, sipped her tea, and plated a brownie for each of us. "Enjoy," she said with a big smile. "While you chew, I will tell you of what is in my heart and mind.

"When they told me how sick I was, I was terrified. Not so much for me, but for you. How could I leave you? How could I abandon you after what had happened to your parents? Not only that, I questioned how I could have let myself get to a place where I was manifesting such a dreaded illness. Cancer of the lungs is all about not being able to take in life. As I sat in deep thought about that, I realized that even though I celebrated every day you were in my life, I'd never let go of my grief over the loss of your parents, the loss of my daughter. I'd bottled that pain up and locked the bottle deep within, thinking I was simply getting on with life. Eventually whatever we bury inside becomes toxic to us. I was at the toxic place. I didn't want to let you down; I didn't want you to think I was suffering. I wanted to give you as best I could a happy childhood. I knew you were sad, and I convinced myself that if I showed you I was cheerful, you'd be okay. I know that was a grave mistake. So grave a mistake, it nearly buried me."

Again, she paused to sip her tea. I knew this was not the time for me to offer my two cents or point out her many puns to lighten the moment. I wanted to tell her how loved I felt, how her strength was what helped me get up each day, go to school, and grow.

"You now know, Meems, our thoughts are actually things. Every thought that goes through our head creates its own energy in the world. My sadness was shrouded in such heaviness that when it surfaced, I did my level best to push it back down to the dark place I felt it belonged. If you hide your true feelings you live a lie. As joy filled as I felt to be your grandmother and your guardian, I was living a lie. Lies are a part of a lower vibration. I call it my low self. You can only stay for so long in such a vibration before your physical body begins to deteriorate. When I was diagnosed with cancer I felt as though I'd been given a death sentence on one hand, and on the other hand, I'd been given a severe warning to clean up my act, rewrite my inner script, and get my act together.

"It was a wake-up call to remember we're all so very connected to each other. My suffering was about to bring you great suffering and I couldn't let that happen. I asked your mother to come and be my guide toward finding a better path. I needed her to help me let her go. I also realized my darkness was what kept her away from us both. That too was so unfair to you. This was the reason I insisted that you come with me to the Seekers Body, Mind, and Spirit Expo. In my heart of hearts, I knew it was time for you to open to all of your gifts and for me to stop being the energy that blocked you. For all of this I'm deeply sorry. I promise you I'll walk a brighter path from here on out. It was your love and belief that helped me to heal my disease. It still makes me sad that your mother and father were taken so young in life. A parent never wants to bury their children. The other sadness here is that I forgot that they were simply on the other side of the veil, that they'd only left their physical vessels and gravity. We're all eternal beings. Our inner light never goes out. I should've been teaching you that all this time. Thank goodness you chose Artie and Bitsy at the expo. Of all the readers there, they were the perfect teachers for you. I stepped back to allow for your wisdom to rise to the surface. I'm so very proud of you. You used that wisdom. Then you had the courage to begin to take classes. I'm kind of glad I was 'chemo weak' and wasn't able to go with you. That level of learning had to be your own. When I was with you at The Nook, your mother made sure to make her whispers heard. When she came to me this last time at Thanksgiving, I know you knew we were in serious discussion and that you wanted and needed to know what we had our heads together about. It wasn't the time to tell you. Now it is. She was working to make sure I'd truly accepted my lessons, released my deep grief, and was on a path climbing the mountain of life instead of stagnating at the foot of the mountain as I had for so long.

"I felt myself changing, healing, and surrendering. I felt for the first time in a long time I'd found my higher self and would live in that place rather than in the dark. I was waiting for the doctor's appointment for confirmation that I'd changed the path I'd been on. As Moraine and I worked through my Reiki appointments I began to realize I had the power to heal. Not only was she amazing at channeling healing energy, she was able to look into my Akashic Records and describe what was written there. Evolution can sometimes be painful. It all depends on what we're thinking, or what we're avoiding thinking about.

"There's so much in life I want for you. However, those are my wants and I will not impose them upon you. So, I'll settle for wanting whatever it is that you want. You're one of the brightest lights I know and there are so many experiences yet to come for you. My hope would be that you greet them all at your highest vibration. Listen, Meems, to the whispers on the wind. They'll be your spirit guides and guardians bringing you the exact knowledge you need to live your best life."

33

Keep Going, Keep Going, Keep Going

I was dumbfounded, speechless. There wasn't anything to say. Gran had held so much inside her for so long. At the moment I was struggling not to bring in the feeling of guilt. I knew from the classes I'd taken at The Nook that guilt was a waste of time and energy. Gran had chosen her path. She made her choices with me in mind, yet they were her choices. I would not now allow myself to shoulder any burden. Part of me was glad, honored that she shared such deep thoughts and feelings with me; another part of me felt raw and unprotected. It was time for me to suck it up, grow up, and step onto a new path just as Gran had done. In my mind's eye I can see White Sage nodding at me.

I know the journey of life is all about experiences. I'd certainly had some already that left indelible marks on my heart and spirit. I also know it isn't what happens to us that determines how things go, it's how we react to and handle what comes to us that matters. I've got my work cut out for me and the rest of my life to keep learning the lessons and applying them to my thinking, my life.

As I sat across from Gran, I took her hand, brought it to my lips, and kissed it. I nodded my head, closed my eyes, and listened to the whispers on the wind. And there they were!

"Good girl," I heard. "You're on the right path. Keep going, keep going, keep going. Trust your inner voice."

Then all was quiet, for the moment!

34

Whispers Can Be Loud

Six months, one year, eighteen months and Gran remains cancer free. As I drift off to sleep my thoughts turn to the fact that I'm coming to the end of my second year of college. At The Nook, one of the conversations with students was that time wasn't real. With the last two years flying by so fast, it would seem that time is an illusion after all. I'm not sure how we've come so far from where we were. Healthy and happy, on a journey we could never have dreamed of when I was in high school. As Gran's health and strength returned, she set her sights on becoming a very involved aspect of The Nook. She actually joined the school and studied to be a certified medium. The combination of a lifetime of learning blended with the amazing courses taught at The Nook served to bring Gran the diploma she sought. Now she's begun to teach classes to those seeking the path to higher consciousness and her dream of becoming an integral part of The Nook has come true. Artie and Bitsy always talked about how three women could move mountains. Gran became a part of their mountain.

My junior year of school is right around the corner. All my liberal arts classes are completed, my average continues to be a 4.0, and I have to choose my last two years of courses based on the degree I want to graduate with. How am I supposed to know which direction I want my life to take?

"Psst, Meems, really? All you had to do was ask," Hermes, my doctor of philosophy, whispers in my ear. "We've been waiting for you to ask! You know we know what your future occupation is, and we will happily share it with you. You also know you have to ask. Which you just did! Look into the degree specializing in nonverbal communication. There are many who need guidance, wisdom, and more effective communication skills. You'll move through the third dimension helping the masses to hear the whispers on the wind. Just imagine."

Marsha G. Cook grew up in Philadelphia, Pennsylvania and at the age of five was known to chat with her maternal grandmother; often telling her mother that Nanny Angel was sitting in the corner and all 'mom' had to do was talk to her. After raising six adopted children, Marsha returned to the work force as a YMCA director. Obtaining both  a bachelors and master's degree in holistic nutrition at the age of fifty, she then studied and became ordained as a non-denominational minister with a doctorate in metaphysics and spirituality. This led to a decade-long foray in teaching and co-directing an accredited school of metaphysics and meditation center known as The Nook. Marsha considers herself a 'seed planter', helping people to discover there is more to our world than meets the eye.

uncommon publishing

IngramElliott is an award-winning independent publisher with a mission to bring great stories to light in print and on-screen. We publish stories that will translate well into film, broadcast, and streaming television projects across many popular genres.

We look for a great story, unique voice, and the author's ability to build a strong platform. Please review our current submission guidelines and check out our latest releases.

www.ingramelliott.com

CPSIA information can be obtained
at www.ICGtesting.com
Printed in the USA
LVHW011942241020
669606LV00012BA/603